IT'S TIME FOR CHRISTMAS

BY ELIZABETH HOUGH SECHRIST AND JANETTE WOOLSEY

It's Time to Give a Play
New Plays for Red Letter Days
It's Time for Thanksgiving

BY ELIZABETH HOUGH SECHRIST

Poems for Red Letter Days
One Thousand Poems for Children
Thirteen Ghostly Yarns
Heigh-Ho for Halloween
Christmas Everywhere
Red Letter Days

IT'S TIME FOR
CHRISTMAS

Written and Compiled by
Elizabeth Hough Sechrist and Janette Woolsey
Decorations by Reisie Lonette

MACRAE SMITH COMPANY: PHILADELPHIA

Library of Congress Catalog Card Number 59-13255
Manufactured in the United States of America

5910

Second Printing

ACKNOWLEDGMENTS

The authors wish to express their thanks and appreciation to the following authors and publishers for their kind permission to include their works in this volume:

The Atlantic Monthly *and* Marjorie L. C. Pickthall *for* "The Worker In Sandalwood" *by* Marjorie L. C. Pickthall; *Francesco M. Bianco for* "The Little Guest" *by* Margery Williams Bianco; *Aileen Fisher for* "Suddenly Flowers In The Meadow;" *Harper & Brothers and* Ruth Sawyer Durand *for* "Gifts For The First Birthday" *from* THIS WAY TO CHRISTMAS *by* Ruth Sawyer, *published by* Harper & Brothers, *copyright 1916,* Harper & Brothers, *copyright 1944,* Ruth Sawyer Durand; *Houghton Mifflin Company for* "Song Of A Shepherd Boy At Bethlehem" *by* Josephine Preston Peabody *from* THE COLLECTED POEMS OF JOSEPHINE PRESTON PEABODY, *and* "Joy Of Giving" *by* John Greenleaf Whittier; *Emilie E. King and* Child Life *for* "The Boy In Nazareth" *by* Emilie E. King; *Alfred A. Knopf, Inc. and* Elizabeth Yates McGreal *for* "The Young Hans Christian Andersen" *by* Elizabeth Yates *from* THE SHINING TREE *published by* Alfred A. Knopf, Inc.; *J. B. Lippincott Company for* "Six Green Singers" *by* Eleanor Farjeon *from* POEMS FOR CHILDREN *by* Eleanor Farjeon, *copyright 1951 by* Eleanor Farjeon, *published by* J. B. Lippincott Company, *and* "The Tree That Didn't Get Trimmed" *by* Christopher Morley, *from* ESSAYS *by* Christopher Morley, *copyright 1919, 1947 by* Christopher Morley, *published by* J. B. Lippincott Company; *Elizabeth-Ellen Long for* "Discarded Christmas Tree;" *The Macmillan Company for* "Post-Christmas Rhyme" *by* Rachel Field *from* POEMS *by* Rachel Field, *published by* The Macmillan Company; *Margaret E. Sangster and* Good Housekeeping *for* "Anniversary" *by* Margaret E. Sangster; *George Sharp for* "The Little Blind Shepherd;" *The Viking Press, Inc. for* "Words From An Old Spanish Carol" *from* THE LONG CHRISTMAS *by* Ruth Sawyer, *copyright 1941 by* Ruth Sawyer, *reprinted by permission of The Viking Press Inc.;* Whittlesey House *for* "To A Christmas Tree" *by* Frances Frost, *with permission of* Whittlesey House, *from* THE LITTLE WHISTLER *by* Frances Frost, *copyright, 1949 by* McGraw-Hill Book Company, Inc.

To Our Friend and Publisher

DURANT L. MACRAE

PREFACE

In this book we have tried to present Christmas as Christ's birthday rather than from the Santa Claus point of view. In searching out the history of Christmas—its customs, legends and celebration—it is easy to see that Santa Claus and his associates are of fairly recent origin. Far older are the Christmas crèche, the carol singing, the lights and decorations of Christmas, the celebration of Epiphany, and many other features. We have planned the material for this book with the hope that boys and girls may be aware of the true meaning of Christmas.

The traditional tales told here have been adapted from many sources. So many stories have been told about Christmas throughout the years that it is hard to know where fact leaves off and legend begins. Some of the traditional stories we have chosen are a combination of both.

The carols in this book are those that we feel are the most familiar to young people. To create a feeling of intimacy with each carol we have tried to tell something about the composers and under what circumstances the carols came to be written.

The first stories chosen deal with Christ in four phases of His life: His birth, His first birthday, His boyhood and His preaching years.

This volume is one more among the many hundreds that have already been written about Christmas. In such a company of fine volumes we can only hope that our book may add something useful to the material already available, and also that it will bring a message to all its readers of fellowship and good will and peace on earth. In the words of the carolers:

"God rest you merry, gentlemen, Let nothing you dismay,
Remember Christ our Savior was born on Christmas Day."

JANETTE WOOLSEY
ELIZABETH HOUGH SECHRIST

CONTENTS

The Nativity

THE NATIVITY *by Elizabeth Hough Sechrist*   19

THE HISTORY OF CHRISTMAS *by Elizabeth Hough Sechrist*   23

Legends and Traditional Stories by Janette Woolsey

ST. FRANCIS AND THE FIRST CHRISTMAS CRÈCHE   31

THE LEGEND OF LA BEFANA   33

THE HOLY FAMILY AND THE GREEDY WOMAN   35

THE STORY OF ST. LUCIA—SYMBOL OF LIGHT   39

LEGENDS OF THE UNDERGROUND BELLS   42

LEGENDS OF THE FLOWERS   43

LEGENDS OF THE TREES   49

THE CHRIST CHILD AND ST. CHRISTOPHER   54

ST. NICHOLAS *by Elizabeth Hough Sechrist*   58

Christmas Customs by Elizabeth Hough Sechrist

THE CHRISTMAS CRÈCHE   67

THE LIGHTS OF CHRISTMAS   75

CHRISTMAS GREENS   83

THE CHRISTMAS FEAST   92

THE ANIMALS OF CHRISTMAS   101

THE GIFTS OF CHRISTMAS   108

The Carols and Their Composers by Janette Woolsey

O COME, ALL YE FAITHFUL   121

JOY TO THE WORLD   125

CONTENTS

HARK! THE HERALD ANGELS SING — 129

IT CAME UPON THE MIDNIGHT CLEAR — 133

O LITTLE TOWN OF BETHLEHEM — 137

AWAY IN A MANGER — 140

WE THREE KINGS OF ORIENT ARE — 143

GOOD KING WENCESLAUS — 146

I HEARD THE BELLS ON CHRISTMAS DAY — 149

SILENT NIGHT — 154

Christmas Poems

WORDS FROM AN OLD SPANISH CAROL
translated by Ruth Sawyer — 161

SIX GREEN SINGERS *by Eleanor Farjeon* — 162

HE CAME ALL SO STILL *Unknown* — 163

THE JOY OF GIVING *by John Greenleaf Whittier* — 163

TO A CHRISTMAS TREE *by Frances Frost* — 164

THE SONG OF A SHEPHERD-BOY AT BETHLEHEM
by Josephine Preston Peabody — 165

SUDDENLY FLOWERS IN THE MEADOW *by Aileen Fisher* — 166

SING HEY! *Unknown* — 167

THE TWELVE DAYS OF CHRISTMAS *Unknown* — 168

A CHRISTMAS HYMN *by Christina G. Rossetti* — 172

THE OXEN *by Thomas Hardy* — 172

MY GIFT *by Christina G. Rossetti* — 173

THE THREE KINGS *by Henry Wadsworth Longfellow* — 174

DISCARDED CHRISTMAS TREE *by Elizabeth-Ellen Long* — 176

POST-CHRISTMAS RHYME *by Rachel Field* — 176

CONTENTS

Christmas Stories

THE LITTLE BLIND SHEPHERD *by George Sharp* 179

GIFTS FOR THE FIRST BIRTHDAY *by Ruth Sawyer* 194

THE BOY IN NAZARETH *by Emilie E. King* 198

ANNIVERSARY *by Margaret E. Sangster* 204

THE WORKER IN SANDALWOOD *by Marjorie L. C. Pickthall* 214

THE YOUNG HANS CHRISTIAN ANDERSEN *by Elizabeth Yates* 222

THE FIR TREE *by Hans Christian Andersen* 229

THE TREE THAT DIDN'T GET TRIMMED
      by Christopher Morley 238

THE LITTLE GUEST *by Margery Williams Bianco* 243

INDEX 251

IT'S TIME FOR CHRISTMAS

THE
NATIVITY

The Nativity

The story of Christ's birth is told in the Gospels of St. Matthew and St. Luke:

And she brought forth her first-born son, and wrapped him in swaddling clothes, and laid him in a manger; because there was no room for them in the inn.

And there were in the same country shepherds abiding in the field, keeping watch over their flock by night.

And, lo, the angel of the Lord came upon them, and the glory of the Lord shone round about them: and they were sore afraid.

And the angel said unto them, Fear not: for, behold, I bring you good tidings of great joy, which shall be to all people.

For unto you is born this day in the city of David a Saviour, which is Christ the Lord.

Now when Jesus was born in Bethlehem of Judaea in the days of Herod the king, behold, there came wise men from the east to Jerusalem,

Saying, Where is he that is born King of the Jews? for we have seen his star in the east, and are come to worship him.

. . . and, lo, the star, which they saw in the east, went before them, till it came and stood over where the young child was.

When they saw the star, they rejoiced with exceeding great joy.

And when they were come into the house, they saw the young child with Mary his mother, and fell down, and worshipped him: and when they had opened their treasures, they presented unto him gifts; gold, and frankincense, and myrrh.

[19]

The city of David mentioned in the story is Bethlehem, in Judea. It was here that Joseph and Mary his wife had come to be taxed. *And it came to pass in those days, that there went out a decree from Caesar Augustus, that all the world should be taxed.* Every person was required to go to his own city to be registered. Joseph, therefore, who was of the house of King David, had made his way back to his ancestral town in the hill country in obedience to the law. And when he and Mary had come to Bethlehem, many people were there for the taxing, and they found the khan, or inn, crowded. Every available bit of space had been taken, and even before darkness had fallen over the little city, sleeping mats covered the floors and courtyard of the inn. When night came upon them and sharp winds blew coldly across the hills of Moab, there was no shelter for Mary and Joseph save only the place where the cows and sheep were stabled.

And it happened that when Mary was delivered of her Son there was no place to cradle Him. So she wrapped Him about with swaddling clothes, and laid her Babe in a manger. No lights were there except for the stars, of which one shone exceedingly bright. No heat was there, except from bodies of the cattle with which they shared the limestone cave. No trumpets blared; no messengers rushed forth to shout the news to all the world that Christ the King was born! No messenger, that is, except one: the angel of the Lord. The angel appeared to shepherds who were watching their flocks in the fields. *Behold*, said the angel, *I bring you good tidings of great joy, which shall be to all people.*

And when the awe-struck shepherds heard the tidings, how Christ was born in Bethlehem, they listened in great wonder, and were overcome with desire to see the Holy Child. They listened while the angel spoke further: *And this shall be a sign unto you; Ye shall find the babe wrapped in swaddling clothes, lying in a manger.*

Then the wondering shepherds saw and heard a host of angels *praising God, and saying, Glory to God in the highest, and on earth peace, good will toward men.* And they marveled that God's messengers had spoken to them.

Let us now go even unto Bethlehem, and see this thing which is come to pass, which the Lord hath made known unto us.

And thus it was that the watchful shepherds of the sheep were the Holy Infant's first visitors. With all haste they departed and went to the lowly cattle shed where they *found Mary, and Joseph, and the babe lying in a manger.*

And the shepherds related to others what they had seen, and what the angel had told them concerning the Child, that this was Christ the Lord.

Then came the Wise Men who were kings of the East, seeking the Child. These were Melchior, ruler of Nubia and Arabia; Caspar, king of Tarsus; and the dark-skinned king of Ethiopia, Balthasar. With the faith of their fathers to give them purpose, and the wisdom of all the ages that had gone before to lead them, they followed the bright Star of Bethlehem. And when it was most bright, and seemed to halt in the heavens, the three kings found that they had come to the place where the young Child was.

In searching for the new-born King, these three potentates of eastern dominions had traveled far. St. Matthew relates that when they had found the place of the Star, *they rejoiced with exceeding great joy.* In their great happiness at the accomplishment of their mission, they fell to the ground. Their joy and relief must have been overpowering, and the impulse to worship overwhelming. After adoring the King of Heaven they rose and opened their gifts, and presented them to Him. The first gift was gold, that precious metal associated throughout the ages with the power of kings. Its luster, like gleaming sunshine, was symbolic of the light that was forever to shine from the Child in Mary's lap. The second gift presented was frankincense, symbolizing Christ's divinity. The frankincense of the East was a rare and sacred resin obtained from a tree that was said to be protected by winged serpents. The burning of this substance was often reserved for the holy of holies, and when the wise men presented it to Jesus they were accepting Him as their King of kings. The third gift was myrrh. This was another rare gum resin, also taken from a plant. Unlike the other gifts, this offering must have quickened the pulse of the mother of Jesus, perhaps even filling her with sudden foreboding. For among the Hebrew people myrrh was a substance used in preparing the dead for burial. It was prophetic of the death of Christ on the Cross of Calvary, an event that was to change the world.

Having presented their gifts to the Child, the Wise Men departed into their own country.

And this was the first Christmas.

THE HISTORY OF CHRISTMAS

When Jesus was born, there began a new era in the world. His birth was an event so important that time seems to have stood still at the moment of the Nativity. Indeed, the calendar of recorded history is divided by the supposed date of His birth. Christian historians long ago agreed upon this division in time by reckoning the years after His birth as A.D. (*Anno Domini,* Latin words meaning "in the year of our Lord") and the age before His birth as B.C. (Before Christ.)

Although we celebrate Christmas on December twenty-fifth, the actual date of Christ's birth is not known. For three hundred years His birthday was observed at various times of the year. In the East it was usually celebrated in spring, while Christians of Western Europe observed it in November or December. Then in 337 A.D., Cyril, Bishop of Jerusalem, was given permission by the Pope to make an effort to determine once and for all a date for Christmas. Such a decision was not an easy one, apparently, for it was several years before the matter was settled. However, Bishop Liberius of Rome announced in the year 354 that the date agreed upon was December the twenty-fifth. Since then Christmas has been observed on that date by Christians everywhere, excepting those who still use the Old-Style, or Julian Calendar. In the Greek, Russian, and Ukrainian Orthodox Churches, Christmas is celebrated on January seventh.

Since there was no written record of the date of Christ's birth, it is easy to understand why the argument went on for several years before a final day was set. Let us see why December the twenty-fifth was probably chosen.

[23]

All over the vast Roman Empire before the Christian era, the people for centuries had held festivals in honor of the pagan gods of nature. One of these celebrations was the Saturnalia, a gay festival held during the winter solstice in honor of the harvest god, Saturn. He was the legendary ruler of Italy during its "golden age." The custom of keeping this festival was so strong that even after Christianity had come into the world the Saturnalia was still celebrated by some of the people. In pondering over their choice of a date for Christ's birthday, the early churchmen saw in this festival a way to give new meaning to an old holiday. The birth of Jesus Christ had brought the light of truth into the world. Christ was the Light of the World. What could be more suitable, then, than to give the old pagan festival a new and wondrous meaning? The Roman Saturnalia ended on December the twenty-fifth. This date was chosen to celebrate Christ's birthday.

Christmas is the most beloved and widely celebrated holiday of our calendar. For weeks before the great day, the Christian world prepares for it. From the smallest villages to the largest cities the streets come alive with bright lights and festive decorations. Christmas trees and greens and holly with bright red berries are on sale in whatever space is available to the Christmas-tree merchants. Every town has its shining community Christmas tree erected in the square where it can be enjoyed by everyone who passes. Store windows look like pictures out of a fairy book, with wonderful scenes that attract crowds of children and grown-ups. There are life-size figures of characters from Santa Claus's workshop and from fairyland itself. There are marvelous miniature scenes of the Nativity, with all the figures of the Holy Family and the shepherds and the Wise Men. The toy departments of the large stores offer every kind of toy imaginable, including many new ones no one has ever before imagined! In the residential districts the houses and lawns seem to vie with each other with their festive decorations and gaily lit trees and shrubbery. It is safe to say that no town in all of America lies dark beneath the

Christmas skies. Lights, lights everywhere this blessed Christmas time! Lights from streets and shop windows and the community Christmas tree in the center of town! Lights from a large cross erected on a hillside above the city! Lights from countless windows in millions of houses across the nation! They shine through the night with steadfast gleam to proclaim a joyful message: Christ is the Light of the World.

It is hard to realize that Christmas was not always the beloved holiday we know today. For many years it was observed only in the churches. But outside the Church when the people celebrated the day most of them were following the ancient custom of observing the winter solstice. From the Romans and the Celtic Britons the customs came, and from the Teutons, and Scandinavians, and even from ancient Egyptians and Persians. So strong was the influence of all these old heathen customs that the people seemed unaware of or indifferent to the true Christian significance of the holiday. It took hundreds of years for the real meaning of Christ's birthday to reach the people. And it took hundreds more

to convince them that Christmas was a festival not only of the Church, but of the homes and hearts of all the Christian world.

During its history of nearly two thousand years, Christmas has passed through good times and bad times. For instance, there was a time when it was against the law to keep Christmas! But this was after the holiday had reached its height. In the days of Queen Elizabeth I, all holidays and holy days were celebrated with intense enthusiasm, especially by the people of rural communities. It was their lot to work hard from sun-up to sun-down for a scanty living. Life for them held few rewards and little pleasure. But holidays were fun days! The farm people could leave their labors in the fields and, for the moment, forget privations and heavy taxation. So they made the most of their holidays, stretching them out as long as they dared, celebrating not for one day only, but on some occasions for a full week. Such a holiday was Christmas—a carnival of fun including feasting, singing, frolicking and dancing. It was at this time that the strange stepchild of Christmas, the Lord of Misrule, came into being. Strangely enough, the Lord of Misrule came into popularity through a centuries-old tradition of the Church. This was the innocent custom of appointing a Boy Bishop to preside over the church services on Christmas Day. The Boy Bishop originally had been chosen because of his good character. He was highly favored to have been chosen, and the young lads whom he appointed as his officers were likewise highly honored. But with the years the custom had gradually changed for the worse. In the England of Elizabeth the First, the Boy Bishop had become a lawless tyrant who ruled over a rowdy and boisterous crowd. Lord of Misrule, they called him, and he and his aides, the Fool and the Jester, lived up to their names. It was they who planned the Christmas carnival and parades, with mummers, musicians and masked rioters. The merrymaking crowds forgot the meaning of Christmas. They desecrated the day.

This was the time when Puritanism appeared in England. The Puritans, a stern and pious sect, looked upon this boisterous manner of observing Christmas with horror. Finally the time came when their influence in the government was sufficient to put a restraint upon the lawless celebration of holidays. In 1643 Parliament abolished Christmas from the calendar altogether, along with Easter and Whitsuntide. And in the American colonies the same repressive measures were used by the Puritans of New England. A law was passed in Massachusetts Bay Colony that forbade the observance of Christmas, making it a prison offense. The colonists were ordered not to be idle on Christmas Day, but to go about their daily work as usual. Christmas could not be mentioned, even in the church.

The law forbidding the keeping of Christmas was passed in 1659. It was two hundred years before Massachusetts recognized Christmas. Finally, about the time of the Civil War, the New England states began to celebrate the holiday for the very first time in their history.

Though Christmas was unrecognized by the New England colonies, the holiday was by no means forgotten in other parts of the New World. In the colony of New Amsterdam, which is now New York, the children not only knew about Christmas— they also knew about Saint Nicholas! Saint Nicholas was patron saint of Holland, the land from which these Dutch settlers had come. They had a very special day for him on December sixth. On that day the good saint was supposed to visit the homes of all good girls and boys, and bring them gifts. In the Delaware colony where Swedish children lived, and in Pennsylvania where there were German, Scotch, Irish and Swedish settlers, gifts were usually exchanged on Christmas Day. The Germans called Saint Nicholas "Kris Kindle." The Dutch called him "Sinter Klaas." Then the English settlers in all the colonies learned of Christmas and the happy little Christmas elf who added such huge enjoyment to its celebration. Whether he was Saint Nicholas, or Kris Kindle, or Sinter Klaas, his appeal to all American children was tremendous! Before long they were calling him Santa Claus.

After the Civil War, and particularly after the turn of the century, Christmas in America grew and grew. The demands grew and grew for all the things that the people wanted to make their Christmas celebration a success, and so a whole new industry came into existence. The Christmas industry supplied evergreen trees and Christmas greens, tree trimmings of all descriptions, Christmas lights and candles, Yuletide gifts and Yuletide greeting cards. In our time, work for millions of people is provided by the Christmas industries. No longer is it possible for Christmas to be ignored or forgotten! No other holiday is prepared for so far in advance, so eagerly awaited, or so joyfully celebrated. Christmas has truly come into its own.

When all the preparations for Christmas are completed—the last greeting card sent off, the last gift wrapped, the cakes and pies and roast turkey ready, the tree illuminated with its colored lights, and the hour of midnight close at hand—then come the Christmass carolers. If we are lucky enough to hear them, or perhaps to be a part of one of the groups who sing the old, old carols on this night, it is then that we remember the real reason for our celebration of Christmas. This is Christ's birthday, the anniversary of that night so long ago when *she brought forth her first-born son . . . and laid him in a manger.*

In the little Judean town of Bethlehem at the Christmas season there are thousands of visitors each year, pilgrims who have come to the birthplace of the Christ Child. They make their way to the Church of the Nativity which long ago was built over the sacred place. First they enter the historic Latin Chapel, built fourteen centuries ago. Then, descending into the Grotto of the Nativity, they see a small recess in the wall. And there, in the floor, is a silver inlaid star marking the traditional place of His birth. Around the star is a Latin inscription stating, HERE, OF THE VIRGIN MARY, JESUS CHRIST WAS BORN.

Many travelers have seen the place. Many, many more have not. But to all who love the Christmas season the truth of His birth is just as real and the message just as appealing: "Jesus Christ was born."

LEGENDS and TRADITIONAL STORIES

BY JANETTE WOOLSEY

St. Francis and the First Christmas Crèche

Many years ago, on a cold winter day in December, 1223, a poor friar was seen walking toward the town of Greccio. There was a feeling of snow in the air and yet he seemed unmindful of any discomfort. Now and then the Brother stopped and stretched out his hand so that the birds flying about him could dart down and perch on it to eat the crumbs that he always carried for them. The sight was not an unusual one, for wherever he went St. Francis, as he was later known, was surrounded by birds and animals that flocked around him unafraid. "Little Brothers and Sisters," he affectionately called them, and protected them from all harm.

As he walked along on this December day he was lost in thought. For he was on his way to preach to the people in the town of Greccio on Christmas Eve, and he was thinking of what he could say to them to impress them and make the Christmas story live in their hearts forever. How could he do this? He remembered his own youth. He, too, had often been thoughtless of others and had been eager for all the material things that money could buy.

Francis had been born the son of a rich merchant of Assisi. He was a delicate little boy and his father, who adored him, had pampered him and given him all the things he desired. His friends were all as wealthy as he and pleasure was their main object in life. But when Francis was twenty years old, suddenly everything changed for him. It was as though a great light had shown around him and the truth was revealed. He knew then that money meant nothing and that in the sight of the Lord all men, be they rich or poor, are brothers. Renouncing the life that had meant so much to him, he now gave himself up to the service of others. Clothed in the poorest of garments he went from place to place, caring for the sick, helping to rebuild with his own hands churches that had fallen to ruins, and at all times preaching the word of God to everybody he met. The fame of Francis spread over the countryside and whenever it was known that he was preaching people flocked from far and near to hear him.

The December day was drawing to a close as Francis approached Greccio. As the sun went down the wind blew more and more fiercely. In the fields that lay along the roadside there were shepherds tending their flocks of sheep. They had built fires here and there, and men and animals were clustered together around them seeking warmth from the frosty night air. Francis stopped for a moment to watch them, and suddenly the words of St. Luke came to him:

And there were in the same country shepherds abiding in the field, keeping watch over their flock by night.

And then suddenly, as though inspired, Francis knew what he had to do! He must *show* the people the Christmas scene. For there were few books in those days and few people who could read even those. If the people could see as well as hear the Christmas story they would remember it for a long, long time. And now as he walked along the lonely road Francis was busily making plans for his Christmas Eve sermon.

He had a friend in Greccio, Giovanni by name, and it was to him that he confided his plan the next day. Giovanni promised to help him and together they prepared the church for the service.

On Christmas Eve people began to arrive at the church in Greccio. Some journeyed many miles either on foot or in carts. Everyone who was able to come managed in some way, for they were all eager to hear St. Francis. As they entered the church that evening they stopped in amazement and then fell to their knees in adoration. For there before them was the manger scene.

At one end of a crude manger filled with hay stood a live donkey and an ox. At the other end were carved figures of Mary, Joseph and the shepherds kneeling before a crib in which lay an effigy of the Infant Jesus.

And then St. Francis told the people again the wondrous story of the birth of the Christ Child and as they listened they were filled with joy and gladness. They knew that never would they forget the sight of Francis as he stood before the very first Christmas crèche they had ever seen, nor would they ever forget the words of hope that he gave them. For it seemed to them they too had really been in Bethlehem on this Christmas Eve.

THE LEGEND OF LA BEFANA

Many, many years ago in a little village there lived an old woman known to all her neighbors as La Befana. She was not a very friendly person. It was not because she didn't want to be, but because she simply didn't have the time to visit with her neighbors. La Befana was always too busy to spend her time talking about unimportant things. Her little house must be kept spotless. And not only her house but all around it too. Day after day La Befana swept and swept. Even *she* couldn't have told you how many brooms she had worn out. Between making new ones and wearing them out with her endless sweeping, La Befana was always busy.

One morning she was up at daybreak as usual. Sweep, sweep, sweep, went her little broom. Her bright eyes darted back and forth lest she miss a speck of dirt hiding in a corner. Suddenly there was a knock at her door. La Befana sighed impatiently. Now who could that be at such an early hour? And why should anyone interrupt her in the midst of her cleaning? Reluctantly she went to the door and opened it just a crack and peered out. And then in amazement she opened it wide. For there outside in the early morning light she saw a wondrous sight.

Although La Befana had never seen a king in her life she knew that not only one but three were standing before her. Surely no one else could be wearing such beautiful robes or bearing such costly gifts in their hands.

"We have lost our way," said one. "Can you direct us? We are seeking a young child who was born in Bethlehem. We have seen his star in the East and are journeying there so we may offer him our gifts. For it has been spoken by the prophets that one would be born who would be King, and we believe it is he whom we seek."

When La Befana heard these words she was amazed. For she, too, had heard of the prophecy. But she could only shake her head. For she had scarcely been out of her own dooryard and she didn't know the direction they were seeking.

The Three Kings started on their way and then stopped again. One of them turned and said, "Will you not come with us, old woman, so that you too may worship the young child?"

La Befana was startled. Go with them? Impossible! She hadn't yet finished her day's sweeping. She couldn't leave her work undone. She wanted to explain this but somehow she couldn't find the right words. So she only shook her head. And as the Three Kings journeyed onward, La Befana stood in her doorway looking after them until they were out of sight.

Then she went back to her work. But somehow she couldn't seem to care whether she found every speck of dust or not. Her mind just wasn't on her sweeping. She kept thinking and thinking. Why hadn't she accepted the invitation of the Kings to journey with them? She, too, would like to see this young babe who the prophets had foretold would some day be King of the Jews. By evening her mind was made up. She would try to overtake the Kings and go with them to Bethlehem. So early the next morning she started out with never a backward glance at the little home that had meant so much to her.

[34]

But sadly enough La Befana never overtook the Kings, nor did she ever reach Bethlehem. However, every place she stopped where there was a child she would leave a little gift, hoping, hoping that some day she would find the young babe she was seeking.

In Italy today the legend of La Befana is still remembered. On January fifth, Epiphany Eve, in memory of the gifts the Magi brought to the Christ Child, Italian children receive gifts. And the one who brings those gifts is La Befana, the old lady who was too busy with her sweeping to journey with the Three Kings. Some even think that she makes her visits on a broomstick carrying with her a bag of gifts wrapped in her apron. Boys and girls know too, that they must be very very good, for besides her bag of gifts La Befana carries another bag, too. And in this one are lumps of coal for those children who have been naughty!

THE HOLY FAMILY AND THE GREEDY WOMAN

All day long the Holy Family had been journeying. The night before, while still at Bethlehem, Joseph had had a dream in which an angel of the Lord appeared before him telling him to take Mary and the young child and flee into Egypt. At daybreak they had started. But now Mary was growing very weary. The baby, although tiny, seemed heavy in her arms. Joseph, leading the donkey, tried to choose a smooth path. But several times the little beast had stumbled and Mary had almost fallen.

"Be of good cheer, Mary," Joseph said. "There are lights in the distance and they probably come from a small village. No doubt there will be someone there who can shelter us for the night."

[35]

Mary smiled at him. "Do not worry, my husband. 'Tis just that the babe is getting restless from being held for such a long time."

At last the little family came into the village. It was late now and all the houses were dark except two. One was a large house, and bright lights shone through all of its windows. The other was a small cottage with but one dim light.

"Surely the people in this house have plenty of room," said Joseph pointing to the larger house. He went up to the door and knocked gently. Inside he could hear the sound of voices. No one answered his first quiet knock so he tried again, this time a little more loudly.

The door was flung open and a woman stood there. "What do you want?" she demanded rudely. "Can you not see that I have guests? Why do you come knocking at my door?"

"We are seeking shelter for the night," Joseph answered. "We have been journeying all day and my wife and babe are weary."

"Well, seek it elsewhere," the woman fairly shouted. "What do you think this is, an inn?" And she slammed the door in his face.

Joseph returned to Mary and said sadly, "She has no room for travelers such as we. But perhaps the people in this small house will at least allow us to sleep on the floor."

He crossed the road and knocked at the door of the little cottage. Almost immediately the door was opened and a woman stood there. Joseph repeated his request for shelter and at once she replied, "Of course. Bring your wife and child in. What I have I'll share gladly with you."

When the Holy Family entered they saw that, simple though it might be, the little house was spotless. In one corner of the room was a spinning wheel and quite evidently the woman had been working at it late this night.

"I am a widow," she explained. "And I must work hard to earn my living."

In spite of their protests she hurried about preparing some hot food for them and then insisted they take her bed for the night while she slept on the floor.

"I can rest some other time. You have a long journey ahead and know not where you may be when night overtakes you again," she told them.

The next morning the travelers awoke refreshed, and after eating breakfast, prepared to depart. As they were leaving, Mary thanked the woman again for her kindness and said to her, "Whatever wish you make first today, that will be granted unto you."

The woman watched Mary, Joseph and the Child until they were out of sight. Then she sighed, and forgetting Mary's words, thought only of her spinning and the work that lay ahead.

"I must get busy immediately," she said to herself and, sitting down, she began to spin. If only I could spin the finest yarn in all the world, she thought. Oh, how I wish I could!

And then she could hardly believe her eyes. Surely, the texture of the yarn began to change under her fingers. It grew softer and finer and she knew that never in her life had she seen such fine quality.

Soon the news of her product spread far and wide. Merchants besieged her door clamoring for some of the fine yarn and offered her a handsome price for it. It was not long before she became so wealthy that it would never be necessary for her to toil so hard for her living again.

All this time the woman who had refused to shelter the Holy Family watched her neighbor with envy in her heart. How had the poor woman suddenly achieved such wealth? Greedy and selfish as she was she couldn't bear to see anyone who had more than she. Although she had never bothered before to speak to her neighbor she went over to see her. She could control her curiosity no longer.

"What happened to you?" she asked. "How did all this come about?"

[37]

So the woman told about the travelers to whom she had given shelter for the night, and about Mary's parting words.

When the greedy neighbor heard this she was beside herself with anger. To think she had let such a gift slip through her fingers! She brooded about this for a long, long time.

Several years later the Holy Family returned from Egypt and their way once again led through the little village. It so happened that the greedy woman was filling a jar with water at the village well and saw them enter the town. She hastened to meet them and so eager was she to speak to them that she forgot her jar and left it by the roadside.

"I'm so happy to see you," she exclaimed. "I've been so sorry that I had so many guests that night that I had no room for you. I've worried about it ever since. So you must stay with me to-night."

Mary thanked the woman but told her that it was still too early in the day for them to stop and they would continue their journey until nightfall.

The woman's expression as she heard these words betrayed her disappointment. She couldn't bear the thought of not getting the opportunity to wish for great riches. So she said, "As long as I invited you, can you not grant me one wish?"

Mary looked at her for a moment. "Yes," she finally said. "You, too, will be granted the first wish you make."

The woman didn't even wait to thank her. Quickly she hurried home so that she could think very carefully in order to wish for something that would bring her the most wealth. She thought and thought but nothing seemed to satisfy her greed. Suddenly she realized she was hungry. Perhaps she should have a good bowl of soup first. Then she would be able to think better. So she started to prepare it. Now where was her jug of water so she could fill her soup kettle? Then she remembered. She had forgotten it and left it by the roadside when she ran to greet the Holy Family.

"Oh, dear!" she grumbled. "If only I hadn't been so forgetful. I wish I had that jar of water."

She had no more than uttered the words than—SWOOSH! There was the jar of water beside her. She had been granted her wish! And as she looked in dismay at the jar she knew then that greediness and selfishness can never bring happiness.

THE STORY OF ST. LUCIA, SYMBOL OF LIGHT

Many, many years ago, about the year 283, in the city of Syracuse in Sicily, a girl named Lucy was born of rich and noble parents. When she was still very young her father died and Lucy was left in the sole care of her mother, Eutychia.

It was at this time that the Roman Empire was governed by Diocletian. Now Diocletian, although he strengthened his empire by many political reforms, was a tyrannical and cruel emperor. He was very much concerned over the rapid growth of Christianity and believed his empire would be stronger if the old religion survived. And, too, he feared that the Christian church might some day take away from him some of his powers. His persecution of the Christians became an obsession with him and many were put to death.

Lucy, while a young girl, had resolved to consecrate her life to God and had desired to devote all her wealth toward helping the poor. But she had been unable to convince her mother that this was the right thing to do.

Eutychia had been suffering from an illness for quite some time. At last Lucy persuaded her mother to make a pilgrimage to the shrine of the martyr Agatha in Catania. Agatha, an early Christian martyr, had been put to death some fifty years before and a shrine had been erected at the place of her burial. Lucy believed that a miracle might be effected if her mother would beseech Agatha to intercede for her. According to the story, this miracle did take place and now Lucy was able to persuade her mother to give away a large part of their wealth to those who were in great need.

Lucy had resolved never to marry. Nevertheless, as was the custom, much against her will she had become betrothed to a young man. When he heard that she had given away the wealth that he had expected would one day come to him, he was very angry. He denounced her as a Christian to Paschasius, the cruel governor of Sicily.

The guards came to Lucy's house to drag her away to the place where she had been condemned to spend the rest of her life. But she stood still, and try as they would they could not remove her from the spot. Then they gathered firewood and placed it all about her and set fire to it. But she could not be burned either. As a last resort they killed her with a sword. But before her death Lucy predicted the end of the reign of Diocletian, and this actually happened just two years later.

Many years later Lucy was declared a saint, and became the patron of the blind. Her feast day is celebrated on December thirteenth. That date has a special significance in northern countries, and in Sweden especially it has come to be a greatly loved day. For in the north the winter nights are long and the people look forward to the time when sunshine will return once again to brighten their days. According to the old Swedish calendar in use during the middle ages December eleventh was the shortest day in the year, so it was natural that St. Lucia's Day brought special joy. The name Lucia comes from the Latin word *lux*, meaning light. St. Lucia was the symbol of light and a happier season to come.

Another reason St. Lucia's Day has come to be such a gay one is that it is now associated with the Christmas season and is really the happy introduction to a time of festivities. In Sweden a special ceremony is held to commemorate this feast day of the Saint. In each family where there are daughters one is chosen to portray St. Lucia. Early in the morning before the other members of the household are up the mother helps the daughter to get ready. She is dressed in white and wears red stockings and a red girdle. And, most significant of all, on her head she wears a crown that is encircled with lighted candles. In one hand she carries a tray full of special saffron buns with raisins in them to symbolize eyes. These buns are called "Lucia cats." In her other hand she carries a coffee pot. She visits each bedroom and wakens the sleeper with a song, offering him some coffee and a bun. Although she may get some help in managing the coffee pot, if the buns are offered by anyone except the Lucia Bride they will most certainly taste bitter!

Choosing the Lucia Bride is not only a custom for each individual household. Naturally there are some homes where there is no daughter, and there must be a Bride for them too. Sometimes the towns or cities have a contest to choose a girl to represent St. Lucia for all the people. It's not just beauty that must be considered, either. Besides, the girl selected for this honor must be generous and kind like the first Lucia. When the day arrives, the Lucia Bride rides down the street at daybreak on a beautiful float seated on a throne. Around her are her attendants, ladies-in-waiting and knights. Carols are sung, and people roused from their beds by the sound of music hurry to the windows to see the lovely girl with her crown of lights. She is the living symbol of the beginning of the Christmas season, the most joyous time of the year.

Although there are many legends told about bells at Christmas time, some of the most interesting are about bells that ring underground.

The whole idea of people living under the earth has always had a fascination for storytellers. Back in the days of the Vikings in Norse mythology there was a widespread belief that a race of dwarfs lived underground deep down in caverns. In later times many of the folk tales of different countries were centered around this same idea. Moreover it was believed that there were persons living under the sea as well.

It is not surprising that some of our Christmas legends have grown up around this interesting theme. One of these stories concerns a little town in Holland by the name of Been. The inhabitants of this town, sadly enough, were most sinful. One year one of their wicked celebrations took place on Christmas Eve.

Forgetting the real meaning of Christmas, no one would stop merrymaking long enough to give food and shelter to a weary traveler that night. The people, of course, didn't know that the traveler was the Lord who had disguised himself for the visit. So he caused the sea to come in and cover Been. But, so the legend goes, if on Christmas Eve you should take a boat and very quietly go over that spot, and listen hard, you can hear from 'way down below the bells of the church of Been.

England has a legend that is similar, except that in this story the people were not evildoers who were punished. Instead, it was a natural disaster that caused a town to disappear.

According to legend there was a little village in a valley in Nottinghamshire. The people who lived there were deeply religious and one of the customs was to come together each Christmas Day at the village church. There they would listen to the bells ringing merrily to proclaim the glad tidings of the birth of Christ. But one day a terrible thing happened. An earthquake shook the valley. The earth opened up and the entire village was lost to view. But the story was told and believed for many years that if you went there on Christmas Day you could hear the bells of the little church ringing far beneath you. It wasn't a sad tone. No, it sounded quite the opposite. For the bells had a merry ring just as they had many years ago when the people of the little village in Nottinghamshire used to listen to them on Christmas Day.

LEGENDS OF THE FLOWERS

Many of the legends of Christmas that have been told throughout the years are stories about flowers. Because roses are so beautiful it is not surprising that they have been a favorite subject. Here are two of such stories.

THE CHRISTMAS ROSE

It was the night of Christ's birth in Bethlehem. Outside the stable of the inn where the Holy Family had taken shelter for the night, a group of people had gathered. Among these were the shepherds who had heard the angel host and had come to worship the babe. All of them were bearing gifts to give to the Child.

There was also in the gathering a young girl, who saw all these people and joined the group to find out what had brought them here. When she heard their story and knew that the young child born this night had been called the Saviour, she too wanted to go in and worship.

[43]

But she had no gift to offer and tears of disappointment fell from her eyes. As her tears touched the ground, at that place there sprang up a bush and on it was the most beautiful white blossom she had ever seen! She plucked it joyfully and, entering the stable, reverently offered her gift to the Christ Child.

And so, the legend says, that was how the Christmas rose came into being.

There is another legend of the Christmas rose which originated in Sweden. It is the story of Abbot Hans who faithfully tended the garden of his monastery. One day a woman came to the garden who said she was the wife of a robber hiding in the forest. She admired Abbot Hans's flowers but said she had beheld some that were more beautiful than his, for on Christmas Eve the forest in which she lived was transformed into a garden of indescribable beauty. Abbot Hans believed her and wanted very much to see this miraculous happening, but the woman was reluctant to lead him to her husband's hiding place.

Abbot Hans thereupon went to the archbishop and persuaded him to agree that if Abbot Hans could bring back proof of this Christmas Eve miracle the robber would receive a pardon and be allowed to come back to his former home. Thus the woman was persuaded to show Abbot Hans the way to the forest.

The day before Christmas, Abbot Hans started for the forest with one of the lay brothers as a companion and the robber's son as a guide. The lay brother did not want to go and grumbled every step of the way. It was just a trap, he said, and probably they would never reach home again.

Just at dusk they came to the cave where the robber and his family lived. The robber was not happy to see them, for he was doubtful that he would be pardoned and he had not approved of what his wife had done.

As the night came on it grew colder and colder. Suddenly a bell was heard ringing. Everyone ran out of the cave and then, to the great amazement of Abbot Hans, the snow disappeared and the ground was covered with myriads of flowers. The roses were especially beautiful, the most beautiful Abbot Hans had ever seen. Birds sang, and animals that were fierce by nature roamed about in a most friendly fashion.

Then it began to grow lighter and everything grew still. Abbot Hans thought that he must be close to heaven. But the lay brother was terrified. He thought the Evil One had come upon them to tempt them. So he shouted a prayer, and at the sound of his voice the light began to vanish. Once more it grew cold and dark and the snow began to drift down.

Abbot Hans was heartbroken and sank to the ground, overcome with sorrow. But even as he did he remembered the flower he had promised to take to the archbishop as proof of the miracle he had witnessed. He reached under the snow to find a blossom.

When the others reached Abbot Hans he was dead. The lay brother picked him up to carry him home, but as he lifted him he noticed the root of a plant clutched in the Abbot's fingers. Filled with remorse over what he had done, the lay brother planted the root in the monastery garden and tended it carefully. When it finally bloomed, the flower was like a lovely rose and the lay brother took it to the archbishop as proof of the miracle he and Abbot Hans had seen. The archbishop thereupon redeemed his promise to Abbot Hans and pardoned the robber.

THE ROSEMARY

The rosemary has a pleasing odor and at one time was used extensively for Christmas decorations. Its story, too, is among the Christmas legends, and here it is.

According to the Gospel of Matthew the Three Wise Men, after visiting the boy Jesus, were warned by God in a dream that they should not return to Herod as he had commanded, so they returned to their own country another way.

When Herod learned that the Wise Men had not returned to him he was "exceeding wroth," and sent out an edict that all male children in Bethlehem under two years of age should be slain. But an angel of the Lord appeared to Joseph in a dream telling him to take the young Child and his mother and flee into Egypt. And they did.

Now, the legend is that one day the Holy Family stopped by a stream so that Mary could wash the garments of the Baby Jesus. After she had finished, she looked around for a place where she might hang them to dry. Close by grew a rosemary bush, so she spread the clothing on its branches. From that time on, says the legend, the rosemary bush has been blessed with its delicate fragrance.

THE DAISY

It was the night of Christ's birth. The shepherds were gathered together tending their sheep when the angels of the Lord appeared to tell them of the wondrous event that had taken place. Hastily, they prepared to go to Bethlehem so they could see the Holy Child for themselves.

One of them remarked that they would be returning again and would need their fires kept burning. Among the shepherds was a young lad whom they had brought along to do just such tasks for them, so they bade him stay and tend the fires while they were gone.

Sadly he watched them go, for he too wanted to see the Babe of whom the angels sang. Surely, he thought, if he hurried he could get back before the fires were completely burned out. So, putting more wood on the fire, he ran as fast as he could to the stable where the Holy Family had taken shelter that night.

But when he quietly entered and saw the shepherds kneeling in silent adoration, he was filled with a desire to offer a gift to the Baby. But what could it be? He had nothing. Then he remembered that that very day he had seen a little daisy with its head sticking out of the snow as if it had known something miraculous was about to happen and had wanted to see what it was.

The little shepherd boy left the stable quietly and hurried back to the field. Yes, there was the little flower right where he remembered seeing it. He picked it carefully and returned once again to the stable.

When Mary saw him she beckoned him to come closer. When he drew near he reverently placed the flower in the Child's hand. The Christ Child grasped the flower and raised it to his lips—and there where His lips touched it the flower turned a beautiful golden color. And that is why, says the legend, the daisy wears a golden crown to this very day.

THE POINSETTIA

Another flower symbolic of the Christmas season is the poinsettia and it, too, has a legendary origin. This is another story of a boy who wanted to give a gift to the Christ Child.

It was the custom in a certain town in Mexico to take gifts to the church on Christmas Eve and offer them to the Christ Child. On this particular night there was a little boy standing outside the church door. He wanted desperately to go in and join the members of the congregation who were laying their gifts on the altar, but he was poor and he had nothing to give.

But I can at least pray, he thought to himself. And so he knelt down outside the window where he could hear the music coming from the church organ. When he rose again to his feet, to his great amazement he saw in the spot where he had knelt a beautiful plant with scarlet leaves and a yellow flower in their center. He had never seen anything like it in his life, and realizing this was a divine miracle he gently plucked the stalk and took it into the church to lay on the altar.

[47]

The Mexicans called the plant "The Flower of the Holy Night." Years later when an American Ambassador to Mexico, Dr. Poinsett, brought it to the United States it was given his name, "Poinsettia."

WhEN German children sing one of their favorite carols, "O Tannenbaum, O Tannenbaum," they are paying tribute to the little pine tree, which has become symbolic of the Christmas season. There are many legends that tell why the pine was selected for this honor.

One of the oldest stories told is that of St. Boniface.

ST. BONIFACE AND THE DRUIDS

Long ago in ancient Nordic and Celtic countries there were people known as Druids, members of a religious order who worshipped all evergreen plants such as pine, spruce and mistletoe. They believed these plants were sacred to their gods and could protect them from harm. One of their practices was to offer human sacrifice to their gods.

One day as St. Boniface was walking through a forest he came upon a company of Druids gathered together under a huge oak tree. They had with them a little child whom they were about to kill to honor the Norse god, Thor.

St. Boniface, with one touch of the cross he carried with him, felled the oak. Then, turning to the awe-struck band of Druids, he chided them for their belief in human sacrifice. Thereupon he told them the story of Christ who had come into the world to save mankind. Knowing the Druids' love of celebrating festivals with singing and dancing, he pointed to a little pine tree growing nearby and bade them take it home, decorate it gaily and with rejoicing honor the birthday of the Christ Child.

MARTIN LUTHER'S CHRISTMAS TREE

Another widely told legend gives Martin Luther credit for the first Christmas tree.

[49]

One Christmas Eve Martin Luther was returning home after preaching in a nearby town. It was a beautiful night, clear and cold, and the sky was filled with myriads of stars. His way led through a forest, and as he walked along he had the impression that the stars twinkling above him were almost a part of the trees themselves.

It must have been a night like this, he thought, when the angels of the Lord appeared to the shepherds on the Bethlehem hillside.

And suddenly he was filled with a desire to share the beauty of this wondrous night with his family. Upon reaching home, he cut down a small fir tree, brought it into the house, and set it up with candles fastened to its branches. When he lighted them it seemed to him that he had recaptured some of the beauty he had beheld in the forest.

THE WOODCUTTER AND THE CHRIST CHILD

Once upon a time, the story is told, there was a poor woodcutter who lived with his wife and two children in a hut in a forest. Times were hard and there was not always enough to eat in the little house. But even if there was not food, there was one thing of which there was an abundance. And that was love and happiness.

It was Christmas Eve. The little family had just gathered around the table to eat their evening meal. It was not very much, but they were grateful for what they had and bowed their heads to give thanks.

Suddenly there was a knock at the door. Who could it be? Perhaps it was some poor traveler who had lost his way through the forest.

The woodcutter went to the door and opened it. Standing outside in the snow was a little boy, scantily clad and shivering with cold. The woodcutter took his hand and led him into the room. His wife quickly got a blanket and wrapped it around the child's shoulders. They didn't try to question him but contented themselves with giving him some hot food and then tucking him into bed with their own two children. The next morning when the woodcutter awoke, the young visitor was standing in the middle of the room and all around him was a dazzling light.

The woodcutter realized then that their guest had been the Christ Child.

The man sank to his knees beside the bed in awe and reverence but the Child bade him rise. Taking a stick from beside the fireplace, the Christ Child opened the door and stepped outside. Thrusting the stick into the ground, He turned to the woodcutter and thanked him for his kindness. He told him that this stick would become an evergreen tree that would be hung with fruit and nevermore would the woodcutter or his family suffer from hunger at this season.

When He had spoken these words, the Child disappeared. There where He had planted the stick a green tree was growing. The woodcutter knew that indeed, he and his family had been truly blessed.

THE CHRIST CHILD AND THE PINE TREE

Because the lights on the Christmas tree have always been symbolic of the stars, there is a story that tells why they are used on the Christmas tree.

When Christ was born in Bethlehem not only the shepherds and the Wise Men came to honor the young Child. Birds, beasts and plants too, came to offer gifts. Each one had something of his own to offer the Babe. That is, all except one. That one was the pine tree. It had nothing to offer but its needles and they would only prick the Baby and were not at all suitable.

But God saw how disappointed the little tree was, so he told some of the stars to go down and rest on its branches. When they did, the little tree was covered with such radiance that the Child saw it and stretched His arms toward it in happiness.

From that time forth, at Christmas time the little pine tree always bears lights in memory of the night it gave pleasure to the Christ Child.

[51]

WHY THE CHRISTMAS TREE BEARS FRUIT

Every year at Christmas the pine tree blossoms with fruit and other ornaments. It really began, says the legend, when the world was first created.

In the Garden of Eden bloomed the Tree of Life. Its branches bore fruit but Adam and Eve had been forbidden to eat any of it. But Eve disobeyed God and plucked the fruit and she and Adam both ate of it. From that time on the Tree of Life bore no more fruit. Even its leaves changed and grew more and more pointed until they became merely tiny needles. But later God felt sorry for the tree and after Christ's birth he allowed it to bear fruit once a year. And so at Christmastime the pine tree blooms again as it did when it grew in the Garden of Eden.

WHY THE CHRISTMAS TREE WEARS TINSEL

Children love the story about the little spiders and how they helped trim the tree.

It happened early one Christmas morning after the tree had been trimmed and was waiting for the children to see it. Now spiders are very curious so they naturally wanted to see the tree too. Looking at it from the floor would never do. No, they must see it right up close. So they crept all over it until they had satisfied themselves completely. But alas! Everywhere they went they left cobwebs! And when the little Christ Child came to bless the tree He was dismayed. He loved the little spiders, for they are God's creatures too. But He knew the mother who had trimmed the tree for the little children wouldn't feel the same. So He touched the webs and they all turned to silver. And ever since that time Christmas trees are hung with shining tinsel.

WHY THE CHRISTMAS TREE WEARS ICICLES

Sometimes Christmas trees are trimmed with shining icicles. An old story gives a reason for that too.

One night the little Christ Child was wandering through a forest. It was cold and He had nowhere to take shelter for the night. The trees were bare, for they had lost their leaves long ago. But then He saw a pine tree, whose low-hanging limbs offered a perfect shelter from the piercing wind. When the pine tree realized that it was caring for the Christ Child, tears of happiness fell from its branches and as they fell they froze into icicles. In the morning when the sun came out it transformed the pine tree into a vision of dazzling brilliance.

THE GLASTONBURY THORN

According to the Gospel of St. Luke, after Christ was crucified, a good and just man named Joseph of Arimathea asked Pilate for the body of Jesus. He took it down from the cross and laid it in a new stone tomb.

About this man Joseph there has come down to us an interesting legend. Some years after the crucifixion of Christ, the story goes, Joseph's enemies made life so hard for him that he was forced to leave Palestine. So he boarded a ship and sailed for Britain.

The journey was difficult for a man of his years and he was exceedingly weary when he reached the shores of what is now England. He was to meet some friends on a hillside in Glastonbury and while he waited for them he thrust his staff into the ground.

Immediately it took root and branches grew from it, and from the branches green leaves. Joseph accepted this miracle as a sign that he should stay in Glastonbury and preach the gospel of Christ to the native Britons.

Every year after that the Glastonbury thorn tree bloomed and its fragrant blossoms became a symbol of miraculous healing. From that time on, people who were ill journeyed to Glastonbury to touch this tree, which they believed would cure them and restore them to health.

THE CHRIST CHILD AND
ST. CHRISTOPHER

The patron saint of those who travel and those who pray to be saved from earthquake, flood and fire is Saint Christopher. This is his story.

Two hundred years after the birth of Christ there lived a powerful Arabian king. He had a son whom he named Offero, which means "the bearer."

As Offero grew into young manhood he became the envy of his companions, for not only was he taller and stronger than they, but he also excelled them in riding and in throwing the spear. Above all, Offero respected bravery and he was determined that one day he would serve a king who would have no fear of any person or any thing. He decided to leave his home to seek such a master.

Offero did not have any trouble finding kings who were glad to welcome him to their courts. All were eager to have this brave and strong young man one of their company. But none of them ever met Offero's standards of bravery and he never stayed in any place for very long.

At last he found a king who seemed to be so brave that he feared no one, and Offero prepared to devote his life to this monarch. But one day he noticed that in a conversation with the king someone mentioned the name "Satan" and the king turned pale.

"Who is this Satan?" Offero inquired of one of the king's guard.

"Do you not know?" the other asked in a surprised tone. "Satan is the Prince of Darkness and is feared by all men."

"Then it is he whom I must serve," answered Offero. And in

spite of the king's pleading that he remain, he set out once more on his journey.

One day as he was crossing a desert he observed a large company of riders approaching. As they drew near he saw that they were knights dressed in costly raiment. Riding in front on a coal-black horse and wearing a black cloak was one whose arrogant bearing proclaimed him to be the leader.

When they were close to Offero they halted and the leader called out, "Who are you and whom do you seek?"

"I am called Offero," the young man answered, "and I am seeking Satan, the Prince of Darkness."

"For what reason do you seek him?" the stranger asked.

"Because he is brave and all men fear him," said Offero. "I am eager to serve him."

"Then you need seek no longer, for I am he," the man in black replied. "You are welcome to join my band of followers and be one of us."

Gladly Offero accepted Satan's offer and felt proud to be included in such fine company.

When he had been traveling with them for several days they came to a place where two roads met. Close by the road which they desired to take stood a simple cross marking the grave of some Christian pilgrim. When Satan saw this cross, he stopped. A look of terror came over his face and he shook visibly.

"We must change our plans," he at last managed to say. "We shall take the other road even though it's far out of our way."

Offero could hardly believe what he heard. Surely there was nothing in the sight of two sticks in the form of a cross to cause such abject fear in a person. He knew then that he could no longer admire or respect Satan, so he let the company continue on their way without him.

Toward evening, as he journeyed onward alone, Offero saw to his delight that he had left the desert behind and was approaching a river. Not far from its bank stood a lonely cottage and he hastened toward it hoping to find shelter for the night. The door was standing open and as Offero came closer he could see inside an old man kneeling in prayer.

When the old man suddenly realized he was not alone he got to his feet.

"Welcome, my son," he said. "Who are you and why do you travel alone?"

Offero told the hermit his story and when he reached the part where Satan refused to pass the cross, the old man nodded his head wisely.

"Of course," he said. "Satan feared the cross because it is the symbol of Christ, who died for the sins of mankind."

And then he told Offero the story of Christ and when he was finished Offero asked eagerly, "How can I find Him so that I may serve Him? For I know now that it is to Christ that I should devote my life."

The old man answered, "A sign will be given you and you will know."

Offero was eager to start out again in search of Christ but the old man persuaded him to stay.

"If you would like to help your fellow men there is something you can do for them right here. Travelers come to this place to cross the river but sometimes the current is strong and the water deep and they are not able to do it alone. You are tall and you are strong. You could carry them over on your shoulders."

This suggestion pleased Offero, and so for many weeks he assisted travelers by carrying them across the stream on his broad shoulders.

One night Offero was asleep in the cottage he shared with the old man. Suddenly he was awakened by a call. "Offero! Offero!" Was that his name he heard? He sat up and listened intently. "Offero, help me! Offero, help me!" The voice seemed to come from the river.

Offero jumped up and seized his staff, which was lying beside him. He rushed out into the darkness and down to the river bank. There to his great surprise he saw a little boy. When the child saw Offero he smiled, and it seemed to the man that a bright light shone all around.

"Offero, carry me across, will you please?" asked the little boy.

Offero, believing the child to have been separated from some company that had previously crossed, picked him up, set him on his shoulders and stepped into the water.

At first all went well. The boy was not heavy and the current didn't seem too strong. But the farther he went the heavier the child became, until Offero's shoulders were bowed down with his burden. At the same time the waters grew higher and higher and swirled about him with such force that he thought several times he would certainly fall and that both he and the child would drown. But using his staff to steady himself he continued to move forward cautiously, and at last he found he was out of the raging current and safe on the opposite shore.

Offero set the child on the ground and then, dropping his staff, he lay down completely exhausted. Just as he fell asleep, as though from a great distance he heard the child's voice saying, "I am the Christ. You have served me well, for you, Offero, carried me, who bear the burdens of the world, through these waters tonight. And I shall leave a sign so that you will know it is so."

Offero didn't awaken until the sun had climbed high in the sky, but when he stumbled to his feet and looked around, he gasped and then fell to his knees. For there where his staff had lain the night before stood a tall palm tree with leaves, flowers and dates. And Offero knew that this was the sign for which he had been waiting. He had found Christ and would serve Him forevermore.

From that time onward Offero was known as Christopher, Bearer of Christ.

Children the world over know St. Nicholas. In America, this good old bishop of the fourth century is considered the ancestor of Santa Claus. In Europe, millions of girls and boys observe his special saint's day on December the sixth as the beginning of the Christmas celebration. In some places he is called Father Christmas.

His story began many hundreds of years ago in the East, in that part of the world known as the Cradle of Christianity. Nicholas was Bishop of Myra, a city in the province of Lycia, in Asia Minor. Much of his story comes to us through legends, having been handed down through the centuries by word of mouth. The history books reveal only a few facts about him. Though the date of his birth is unknown, he grew up in the town of Patara where he became noted for his Christian piety. When the old Bishop of Myra died, Nicholas, though still a young man, was chosen to take his place. Now it happened that the notoriously wicked Emperor Diocletian was in power during the early part of Nicholas's bishopric. The Emperor was very angry with all those who refused to worship the goddess Diana. When the Christians refused to revere the pagan goddess, they were severely beaten and thrown into prison. Among them was the Bishop of Myra. Dark days fell upon all Christians of the vast Roman Empire. Starved and treated cruelly because of their faith, many died in prison. But Bishop Nicholas survived. Then Constantine the Great became ruler of the empire. Unlike Diocletian, Constantine was sympathetic toward the Christians. In the great battle of Adrianople he had seen a cross, and with it the fiery words: BY THIS CONQUER! This vision convinced the Emperor of the truth of Christianity, and from that time forth he gave his support to the Church. The prisoners were freed, among them Bishop Nicholas. The only other fact about Nicholas that is recorded is the day of his death, December sixth. *The Golden Legend,* an ancient book, gives the year as 343 A.D.

One of the stories about Nicholas tells how he became the youngest bishop of the Christian Church. It is said that when the old Bishop of Myra died there seemed to be no one capable of taking his place. The Church was still having a great struggle against paganism. A bishop must needs be not only a man of God but also a man of great courage and steadfastness. He must also be generous and kind, and able to win converts to the Christian teachings. Where would such a man be found? An important meeting of bishops took place in Myra to elect a man to this high office. But no decision was made and the meeting broke up in discouragement. That night the eldest bishop fell to his knees and prayed long and earnestly to God for guidance. When he finally slept, he had a vivid dream in which a voice spoke to him clearly. "Watch for the first man who will enter the church at matins," the voice commanded. "You will know him, for his name is Nicholas."

When morning came the old bishop told the others of his dream. None of them knew a man by the name of Nicholas. But, prayerfully and hopefully, they waited within the door of the church. And when young Nicholas of Patara came through the door to attend matins, they knew at once that this was the man God had chosen for them.

What kind of man was this Nicholas? We are told that he was kind and generous, steadfast and full of courage. By his good example he was able to win many souls to Christianity. Because of his kindness he was ever mindful of the poor in his parish. There were many of these, for, during his time a great famine had come over the land. Many people starved and grew sick, and many died.

It was at this time that one of the Bishop's most famous miracles is said to have taken place. A poor widow had no bread for her little family. In desperation she sent her three small sons to look for food. The little boys went about begging for bread, but in vain. At last they came to an inn. Here they were permitted to enter, but alas, the wicked innkeeper and his wife slaughtered the lads and placed them in three pickling barrels. After the worried mother had waited a long time and her sons had not returned, she went to Bishop Nicholas with her troubles. Not long after, a tall stranger walked into the inn and demanded to be taken to the three little boys at once. Recognizing the stranger as Bishop Nicholas, the man and his wife were in terror of their lives, and showed him the three pickling barrels. The Bishop straightway restored the boys to life and they were reunited with their mother.

It was also at this time of the famine that Nicholas performed another miracle. Bread was as precious as gold in this wheatless land, when one day several ships sailed into the harbor. It was soon learned that they were laden with wheat and bound for the Emperor's city of Constantinople. They had come into the port of Myra for repairs. Word of the precious cargo that filled every cranny of the big ships spread quickly throughout Myra. The people gathered together. If only some small part of the cargo could be unloaded to keep the little children of their city from starving! It was decided that a delegation should go to the port and beg the shipmasters to sell some of the wheat. This was done, but the shipmasters refused. Not one tiny grain would they sell! When the disheartened men returned to the town with their news, the people were in a panic. The ships must not be allowed to leave the harbor with all that life-saving grain! It looked as though the men meant violence until Bishop Nicholas intervened. "I shall go to them," he decided.

"What can a gentle man of God accomplish with those hard-hearted seamen!" the people chided. But others answered, "They will listen to Father Nicholas."

And listen they did, respectfully, while he begged for one hundred muyes from each ship to save their starving people. "But we cannot give even one grain, Bishop my lord," the officers told him. And they explained how the cargo had been weighed at Alexandria and must show up at their destination with the weights of each ship exact and entire.

But the good Bishop was not daunted. "Give us but one hundred muyes of grain from each ship, and I promise you on the truth of God that not one grain shall be missing in the weight of your cargoes on reaching your port."

By the strength of his own conviction, Nicholas persuaded the shipmasters. And it was as he had promised, for when the ships reached Constantinople it was said that the weights were right and entire so that not one grain seemed to be lacking. And the wheat went into bread, saving many of those in Nicholas's city from starvation.

The men of those merchant ships may have heard of Bishop Nicholas before they came face to face with him, because of a well-known story that had earned him the respect of seamen everywhere. It was told how, when Nicholas was still a young man, he had made a pilgrimage to the Holy Land to see the place where Christ was born. On his return, while the ship was far out at sea, a fierce storm had raged, and the vessel was tossed about cruelly in the gigantic waves. When the ship began to sink and it seemed as though all aboard her would perish, Nicholas dropped to his knees in prayer. Those aboard told how the vessel had immediately righted herself in the suddenly calm waters, and later came into port safely. It was because of this miracle that Nicholas later became patron saint of sailors. So strongly did the Greek and Russian seamen count on his protection, that for hundreds of years no ship of theirs sailed the seas without an ikon of St. Nicholas.

But how did St. Nicholas become associated with Christmas? There are several reasons why he, among all the saints of the calendar, was gradually adopted as Father Christmas. The legend that is most responsible for his reputation as a giver of gifts is that of the three unmarried daughters. An impoverished noble-man had three daughters who were unmarried because he could not afford to give them dowries. In that day, marriages were ar-ranged by the parents of the young couple. It was the custom for the father of the bride to present his daughter's husband with a sizable dowry. The better the dowry (a sum of money, jewels or land, or perhaps all three) the better the marriage. It was a sad state of affairs indeed if the father of a single maiden could offer no dowry at all. But such was true in this case, so the three re-mained at home, very unhappy with no prospects of marriage in view. Then Father Nicholas heard of their plight, and one day, passing their house, he threw a bag of gold in through the open window. No one was surprised to learn, shortly thereafter, that the eldest girl had been wed to a man of noble birth. Not once, but thrice, the good Bishop made this same generous gesture, with the result that all three of the daughters were wed. It is said that when the third bag of gold was tossed through the window Nicholas was observed by the father. Although he showered the Bishop with thanks, Nicholas begged that he keep the matter a secret, and thus it was that when the story was told in later years Nicholas became known as the secret giver of gifts.

After the death of Nicholas the place of his burial in Myra be-came a famous shrine. Two hundred years later the Christian emperor Justinian erected a beautiful cathedral in Constantinople in honor of Nicholas. But times began to change. The Holy Land, where Jesus of Nazareth had dwelt and where some three cen-turies later Nicholas had driven the pagans from his parish, was now in the hands of the infidel Saracens. And so it was that when a band of forty-seven courageous men fought their way to the tomb of Nicholas in Myra and took the relics of the saint to a new shrine in Bari, Italy, the episode was regarded as a triumph. This "stealing" of the relics resulted in Nicholas's being chosen as patron saint of thieves. For nearly nine hundred years the Cathe-dral of *San Nicola* in Bari has been one of the great shrines of

Christendom. Saint Nicholas Day in that city is celebrated on May ninth, the anniversary of the day his relics were brought to that place.

But St. Nicholas Day in other parts of the world is on December the sixth. Because the children loved St. Nicholas they wanted to keep his saint day. And because December sixth was not too far removed from Christmas Day, he began to be associated with that holiday. The saint was noted for his generosity, a virtue that is closely akin to gift-giving. When, on the Eve of St. Nicholas Day, the children left gifts of hay and carrots on the doorstep for St. Nicholas's white steed, it seemed only natural that he should reciprocate by surprising them with little gifts in return. Often these were disguised to look like carrots or cabbages, but when the vegetables were examined they were found to contain gifts. And so it became customary for gifts to be exchanged on this day. After several hundred years, in most countries this custom of gift-giving was transferred to Christmastime. For most of the children of the world, St. Nicholas began to make his visits to the earth on Christmas Eve, instead of on the eve of December the sixth.

When the Dutch settled New Amsterdam in the New World, they brought St. Nicholas with them. To have left him behind would have been unthinkable. And when they spoke lovingly of good old *San Nicolaas,* it must have sounded very much to other children like Sanna Claus. At any rate, it was not long before the American name of Santa Claus was adopted by boys and girls for this kind, generous old fellow. And then, as Santa Claus, he underwent some changes. From the dignified bishop who wore a long bishop's cloak and mitre and carried a crozier, he gradually turned into a fat, jolly elf who was small enough to come down chimneys! A poet-doctor from New York named Clement Moore wrote a poem that is familiar to boys and girls, and to their parents and grandparents who read it when they where children. In the poem, "A Visit from St. Nicholas," the "right jolly old elf" is described in these well-known lines:

[63]

He was dressed all in fur from his head to his foot,
And his clothes were all tarnished with ashes and soot;
A bundle of toys he had flung on his back,
And he looked like a pedlar just opening his pack.

His eyes—how they twinkled! his dimples how merry!
His cheeks were like roses, his nose like a cherry!
His droll little mouth was drawn up like a bow,
And the beard of his chin was as white as the snow;

The stump of a pipe he held tight in his teeth,
And the smoke it encircled his head like a wreath;
He had a broad face and a little round belly,
That shook when he laughed like a bowl full of jelly.

It can easily be seen that this description is very different from
the centuries-old conception of Bishop Nicholas. But it was the
beginning of our present-day Santa Claus, that descendent of St.
Nicholas who is so real to millions of his followers. Though his
appearance has changed, there is still present in his character that
loving spirit of the beloved saint who lived hundreds of years ago
across the seas in Asia Minor.

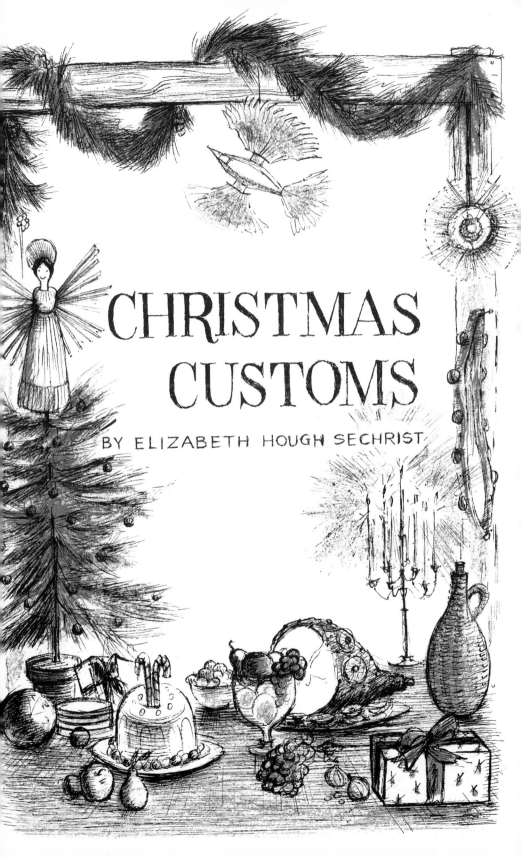

CHRISTMAS CUSTOMS

BY ELIZABETH HOUGH SECHRIST

The Christmas Crèche

Away in a manger, no crib for a bed,
The little Lord Jesus laid down his sweet head.

It is Christmas Eve and preparations are going feverishly ahead in millions of homes across the world to welcome the birthday of the Christ Child. So many things must be done before that first star appears in the evening sky! From the kitchens of the houses come wonderful smells of last-minute baking and cooking. Gifts are in the process of being wrapped, candles and greens are being set in place, and the tree is being trimmed. And there is one other preparation for the birthday that is being repeated in millions of homes, rich and poor, here at home and across the seas. This is the creation of the Christmas crèche, the miniature Bethlehem.

When the children of America bring down the boxes from the attic and unwrap the tiny figures of the Nativity scene, it is nice to know that other people in other lands are doing the same. From the "Bethlehem cave" of the Syrian children in that land where Jesus was born, to the *Jeslicky* in Czechoslovakia around which the children are singing their Christmas hymns, then back to North America where the Mexicans are setting up their beloved *nacimiento* of the *Posada,* all are sharing in a universal gesture of reverence and love. All the figures of the Nativity are there: Mary the Holy Mother, Joseph and the little Baby; the three Wise Men in their royal robes; the shepherds with their crooks; the lowly cattle, the oxen, the asses, the sheep and the lambs. And whether it is erected in the largest of the world's cathedrals or built with simplicity in the crudest of homes, the message of the crèche is the same: Christ was born of Mary, and she laid Him in a manger.

Elsewhere in this story of Christmas we have told how St. Francis of Assisi made the very first crèche for the people of his parish. From that time on, the miniature scene of the Nativity was adopted and beloved by people throughout the Christian world. At first it was used only in the churches, but gradually the crèche was taken into the homes at Christmas to be enjoyed and adored.

In Italy, Spain, Portugal and France the custom grew, and spread to other countries. Swiss and German wood carvers fashioned the tiny figures of the Crib delicately in wood. These were precious to their owners and were proudly handed down from generation to generation.

In Italy *presepe* is the name for the place of the Nativity, though its literal meaning is stable or manger. Since their country was the home of the very first crèche, we can readily understand why this feature of Christmas is so loved by the people of Italy. From that first crèche in 1223 to the present time the custom has been growing. In the years between there have been many wonderful *presepi* in this country of famous artists and artisans. In Rome there is one in the Church of Ara Coeli containing a Bambino (Baby) said to have been carved from an olive tree from the Mount of Olives. Each year at Christmastime thousands of visitors from far and near gather to see it being carried to the top of a long flight of steps for the blessing of the crowds beneath. The *presepe* which has been called the most famous Christian Crib in the world is also in Rome. It is housed in the Basilica of Saints Cosmas and Damian. It was created about three hundred years ago in the city of Naples, and has been handed down through many generations of families to its present owner. The scene covers an area of forty-five by twenty-one feet and shows the

Manger scene, the palace of Herod the king, and farmlands and villages in a fascinating panorama. There are hundreds of wooden figures in the scene, hand-carved by famous artisans of the world. In addition to the central figures of the Holy Family and the other characters of the Nativity story, there are angels and animals, and people busily engaged in the everyday tasks of baking bread, fishing, attending shop. One value of this unusual *presepe* is the fact that it so ably presents a picture of life in Naples at that time in the seventeenth century when the scene was created.

The Bambino of the Christmas scene is often shown in rich costume and adorned with valuable jewelry, all of which have been presented to Him as gifts. Almost all Italian *presepi* are lavish in costume and background, especially those in the churches and cathedrals. Of these, probably none is more extraordinary than that built many years ago by the Capuchin monks. This is the Madonna della Grazie whose figures were carved from wood by the famous artists Gaggini and Maragliano. The manger with the Bambino and the Holy Family are at the base of a sloping grotto, while the figures of the Three Kings and the shepherds and their sheep all move down the mountainside eighteen feet to the stable. This mechanical feat was considered something of a miracle centuries ago and is still today very impressive.

Every Italian home has its own *presepe,* and though the tiny figures are often inexpensive and very simple they are well loved by the children who put them in their places on Christmas Eve. When dusk falls, the candles around the little Nativity scene are lighted and prayers are said by the family. The important moment comes when the mother of the household puts the tiny Bambino in His crib. After prayers, a feast is served, for this day has been a fast day and everyone is hungry. But the family can continue to enjoy the *presepe* as they eat, for the Christmas Eve supper is laid on a table near the manger scene.

In France, most families enjoy two crèches. The first is in their churches at midnight mass on Noël Eve, for even the smallest church has a *mangeoire* in a corner of the chapel with a star suspended above it. But the second, their own crèche, is enjoyed most by the French people. They take great care in setting it up. They gather or buy holly or other greens to use as a background for the scene. When the *Petit Jesu* is placed in the manger with the soft glow of candles and a Star of Bethlehem suspended over the crèche, it makes His birthday seem very real to those gathered around it singing their Noëls.

The Germans call their miniature Bethlehem the *krippe*. German and Swiss families have figurines that are hand-carved in satiny woods. Some of them are very old, having been handed down through the family. The people are justly proud of them. What is probably the finest collection of Christmas Cribs in the world is in Munich in the Bayerisches National Museum.

In Spain, the *nacimiento* takes the place of a Christmas tree as the center of interest at Christmas. The tiny figures may be bought in shops and at street stalls weeks before Christmas. Made of plaster and painted in bright colors, they are quite inexpensive and so can be bought by everyone. Every home has its *nacimiento* and the children gather around it on *Noche Buena,* Christmas Eve. They have special Christmas hymns to sing to the Infant Jesus. And when the Spanish people are happy they always want to dance to show their joy. So, to the sounds of the tambourine, they dance in honor of the Holy Child. When darkness falls, a light is placed before the image of the Virgin. The figures for the *nacimiento* in the churches and cathedrals of Spain are life-size and very magnificent. Many of them were created by famous artists.

In the Spanish language, *posada* means an inn or lodginghouse, but more specifically the inn of the Nativity story. In Mexico, the word has come to mean that wonderful period of nine nights when the *Posadas* are performed. Begun on December sixteenth, they end on Christmas Eve. Nowhere in the world is Christ's birthday celebrated with more enthusiasm than in Mexico. The *Posadas* are the chief feature of the celebration. Sometimes they are held in the same house all nine nights, with only the family or perhaps a few close friends attending. But the Mexicans are a very sociable people and so the more popular way is to combine the celebration with eight other families. Then the enactment of the *Posadas* is held in a different home on each of the nine nights.

There are several reasons why the *Posadas* are so happily looked forward to each year. For one thing, they are an important part of the social season, with the women planning their wardrobes carefully so that they may appear each night wearing a different dress. Also, Christmas is courtship time in this land of señors and señoritas. And who knows? It isn't too unlikely that the partners who enjoy the *Posadas* together will wind up the Christmas season with an announcement of a betrothal. But deeper than either of these reasons is the religious motive, to celebrate the birthday of the Lord.

To get a clear picture of the enactment of the *Posadas*, let's follow the guests who have just knocked on the door of a well-to-do Mexican family on the first night, December sixteenth, when the *Posadas* are just beginning. The house is brightly lighted. When the door is thrown open, everyone is greeted warmly by the hosts of the first *Posada*. As soon as all the guests have arrived they are grouped into characters for the act. One group is called Holy Pilgrims; the others are Cruel-Hearted Innkeepers; two children are chosen to represent Mary and Joseph, another represents the Angel. First of all the host leads in a recitation of prayers to the Virgin Mary. Then everyone, family, servants and guests, is given a lighted candle and told to form a procession. The Angel guides the way through various rooms of the house followed by Mary and Joseph. As they proceed, they sing the Litany of Loretto, a special prayer. At the door of each room the procession pauses while Joseph and the Holy Pilgrims beg to be admitted. But the cruel innkeepers refuse at each door, until they come to the room where the *pesebra* has been erected. Here they are given permission to enter. All gather around the miniature stable with its manger (now empty), its sheep and shepherds, and all the other

[71]

small figures that it has pleased the family to place there. Two children step forward with the statues of Mary and Joseph and put them in their places in the scene. The manger, however, remains empty until the last night of the *Posadas.* Now all kneel about the *nacimiento,* and the *Posada* ends with the singing of several favorite Christmas hymns.

Each night for nine nights the same enactment takes place, with each character doing his or her best to make it a success. The last *Posada* is the most impressive. It takes place on Christmas Eve. When the procession starts through the house on that night, a little girl carries the image of the Infant Jesus in her arms. As usual Joseph begs at each door for admittance:

> *In heaven's name I beg for shelter;*
> *Mary, my wife, can go no farther.*

And at each door he is refused with the words:

> *Begone, begone! No inn is this.*
> *You may be thieves; I do not trust you.*

But at the door of the room where the altar is, Mary and Joseph and the others are admitted. They kneel in reverence before the altar, which has been decorated with tinsel and flowers and surrounded by candles. Then the climax of the evening comes. While a prayer is chanted, the image of the Child is placed in the stable. The people rise and sing to the Holy Babe:

"Alleluia, alleluia! Let us rejoice because the Lord has deigned to come to His people! Let us sing praises to the Lord. . . . Hosanna in the highest!"

A social hour follows in the patio, lasting until it is time to go to midnight mass. But before they leave, everyone returns once more to the *pesebra* to hear the children sing a lullaby to the Christ Child. They whisper to the Child, *"Feliz Navidad!"* (Merry Christmas) and file softly out of the room, leaving only the quietness and the gentle light of candles.

In countless homes all over America a miniature Bethlehem is displayed annually. Sometimes it is set up under the Christmas tree, sometimes in a corner of the room or even on the fireplace mantel. The figures for the crèche can be bought in the stores. Pine or balsam boughs provide a background, while simulated grass and rocks and artificial snow make the scene more realistic. In addition to the Nativity characters there are camels and barnyard animals and birds. Some children put tiny reindeer and horses and people, and even soldiers in their crèche. They add to it what they like, keeping the Holy Family and the manger as the central feature.

Today most of the figurines are made of clay or plaster of paris, then painted. These have become a symbol of the real Christmas to the extent that in some places they are taking the place of Santa Claus in the affection of the boys and girls. In some communities, church groups take on the project of making the miniature Nativity characters. In Bryn Athyn, Pennsylvania, where the beautiful Bryn Athyn Cathedral is the seat of the Swedenborgian sect, hundreds of these little figures are assembled and painted by the women of the church. Months ahead of time they are sent out to distant lands as far away as South Africa so children will receive them in time for Christmas.

Each year in one of the Moravian buildings in Bethlehem, Pennsylvania, there is a wonderful *putz* on display during the Christmas season. *Putz* is the German word for ornament, but to the Moravians and others who have adopted the custom, a *putz* is a homemade miniature Nativity scene. This particular *putz* is a very grand one, with bushels and bushels of moss and a miniature stream running through the rocky terrain; with seven scenes from the Holy Land consisting of more than two hundred buildings; and with, of course, the Holy Family hand-carved from satiny mahogany wood. The *putzen* in the homes, however, are not on such a large scale. They differ according to the taste or particular talents of the creators. But they have several features in common: the unique twenty-pointed Star of Bethlehem, which is always suspended over the hillside scene; a light in the tiny stable where the Babe lies in the manger; and the fact that many of the small figures and objects of the *putz* are very old. The early settlers of Bethlehem brought the idea of the *putz* with them from Germany and it has always been a cherished custom. After Christmas is over the children wrap the figures carefully and help to put them away for another year, knowing that this is what their parents and grandparents must have done to preserve them so well for so many generations.

Although most Christmas Nativity scenes in America are miniature in size, there are some with life-size figures. These are becoming more popular and may be seen in almost every section of the country. They are displayed on the lawns of churches and on college campuses, before the county courthouse and even in the town square, in department-store windows and large lobbies of business buildings, wherever the Holy Family and the Wise Men and shepherds can be grouped. And more than ever before in the history of Christmas decorating, these life-size representations of the crèche can also be seen on the lawns of houses throughout the nation. This change-over in many cases from Santa Claus and his reindeer to the portrayal of the Nativity seems to signify that Americans are relearning the real meaning of Christmas.

> *The Stars in the sky looked down where he lay,*
> *The little Lord Jesus, asleep in the hay.*

And so, throughout the centuries, people have reverently set up their Christmas mangers to show their love for the Holy Child born in Bethlehem so many years ago.

THE LIGHTS OF CHRISTMAS

Christ is, for large numbers of people, the Light of the World. Today His feast is often called the Feast of Lights, especially among members of the Eastern Orthodox Church. To all Christians this term seems very descriptive, for Christmas is indeed a time when darkness seems to vanish while the brightness of millions of Christmas lights gleams meaningfully everywhere.

STARS

The first light of Christmas that usually comes to mind is the starlight of Bethlehem. The Bible story in the words of St. Matthew tells us *there came wise men from the east to Jerusalem, saying, Where is he that is born King of the Jews? for we have seen his star in the east, and are come to worship him.* Then later, *And lo, the star, which they saw in the east, went before them, till it came and stood over where the young child was. When they saw the star, they rejoiced with exceeding great joy.*

In some countries of Europe the fast that precedes Christmas is not broken until the first star appears in the sky on Christmas Eve. Many of our Christmas carols sing of the Star of Bethlehem. One of these is the old Moravian hymn, "O Morning Star." This is always sung at the Vigil Service on Christmas Eve in Moravian churches in the United States.

Each year around Christmas time the large planetariums in our country offer an interesting lecture on the Christmas sky. The mysterious Star of Bethlehem is set against the actual background of the sky as scientists say it appeared on that night nearly two thousand years ago. The data from ancient documents have been coupled with the scientific knowledge of today's astronomers.

The Star of Bethlehem is used often in decorations to represent the night of Christ's birth. From the small stars atop a million Christmas trees in our homes to the huge ones erected on hillsides to shine down on big cities, all are reminders of that "star of wonder." There is one immense star that can be truly called the Star of Bethlehem. Erected annually on South Mountain in Bethlehem, Pennsylvania, it is a huge structure ninety-one feet high, easily visible for a distance of twenty miles. On the other side of the continent, on the mountainside above Palmer Lake, Colorado, a huge star five hundred feet wide is displayed at Christmas time.

In cities where Polish-Americans still observe the customs of their fatherland, the Festival of the Star, or *Pasterka*, is observed in the churches on Christmas Eve, at a Shepherd's Mass. In the state of Alaska, members of the Greek Orthodox Church there carry out the custom of "going around with the star." They carry their illuminated star on a high wooden pole and go from house to house singing carols. Those whose houses are visited by the star-bearers await the singers with hot refreshments to warm them before they go on to the next place.

This custom of carrying a star about on Christmas Eve is observed in a number of European countries. In Rumania the star, or *Steaua*, is decorated with numerous little bells that tinkle as they travel, heralding the approach of the singers. In Norway, this custom used to be performed by Star Boys who collected food and money as they went from house to house. The children of Poland were familiar not only with Star Boys, but also with the Star Man. Usually the Star Man was the priest of the village in disguise. He asked about their behavior during the past year, and if they had been good they were rewarded with presents.

In some places in Holland a procession is formed in the village square, headed by the star-bearer, who is followed by young men dressed in all sorts of odd costumes. They wend their way through the streets of the village singing Christmas hymns. In some places in Europe the Star Boys not only sing carols, but also perform little plays as they travel from place to place. In Sweden the boys carry the star about on Epiphany, "the twelfth day of Christmas," and give a pageant, the same one each year. The boys who represent the three kings dress all in white and wear tall white hats. Among the characters is an ugly long-nosed Judas carrying his bags of silver.

In Mexico, the boys who carry the star on Christmas Eve are a part of the *pastores,* plays performed yearly in that country. They sing with their beautifully trained voices as they proceed from the home of the singing master to the church, carrying the star. The *pastores* were brought to Mexico from Spain long ago.

CANDLES

It was in the land of Syria that the governor, *Cyrenius,* carried out the decree of Caesar Augustus to enroll all the people for

taxation. And it was because of this that Mary and Joseph went to Bethlehem, where their son Jesus was born. Today, in the land of His birthplace, the people of Syria place candles in the windows on the anniversary of His birth to light the Christ Child's way. Placing a light in the window on Christmas Eve is a custom in many places. A tall candle is chosen so that it will burn all night. In some countries the candle is burned again on the eve of Epiphany so that the Wise Men will have light to guide them on their journey.

Candles play an important role in the celebration of Christmas in the churches. Many years ago the Feast of the Purification of the Virgin was chosen by the Pope to be also a day for the blessing of the candles. It came to be known as Candlemas Day and usually was recognized as the end of Christmas festivities. According to our present calendar, Candlemas comes on February second and is observed in Roman and Greek Catholic Churches and in the Protestant Episcopal Church. The blessing of the candles is performed by the clergy in an impressive ceremony.

Candlelight services are held on Christmas Eve in thousands of churches across our nation. One of these services, held especially for children in the Moravian churches of America, is called the Christmas Love Feast. While the organ is playing each child is served with a bun and a cup of hot Sanka. Then, while the music continues, trays of slender beeswax candles are brought down the aisles. These are made by the women of the church. Each child receives one of the lighted tapers, and each holds it below its colored paper frill so that the melting wax will not cause burns. The children are familiar with this candle ceremony and know how to take their parts in it. They have been taught that the light that is being shed softly over the church by the many candles is representative of the light that came to the world with the birth of Christ. Several hours later the church conducts another candle service for adults.

Many years ago in England when candles were the chief source of artificial light, their making was an important part of the housewife's responsibilities. When candle-making time came round the boys and girls in the family helped with this fascinating chore. They were especially interested in the making of the Christmas candles, for these had to be thick and tall and long-lasting. It was considered an ill omen if the candle should burn out before the Yuletide festivities came to an end.

In Ireland it was considered proper for the Christmas candles of the church to be extinguished by a female whose name was Mary. It was preferred, too, that the candles be made of beeswax. Beeswax is made by virgin bees and there was a belief that bees were sent "directly from heaven" to perform this function. In Irish houses, as in many others, Christmas candles were placed in the window to light the way of the Christ Child.

In the Bavarian section of Germany, people place lighted candles in the window on Christmas Eve so that the little Christ Child may find the house and leave His gifts for the girls and boys there who have been good. It was in Germany that candles were first used to decorate the Christmas tree.

In France, in houses and in the churches, lighted candles are used around the crèche. When carol singers go from house to house they carry a small crèche and lighted tapers, for these seem inseparable on the eve of Noël. In Italy, too, the *presepe* is always surrounded by lighted candles. In Spain and Mexico, in addition to the candles that decorate the altar in a house, a lighted taper is often placed above the door.

In Finland, candlelight gleaming from the windows of houses lights the way of the churchgoers in the darkness of early morn, for the services begin at six o'clock when the world is as still and dark as at midnight. However, when the church is entered the gloom disappears, for here there are numerous candles to throw out a warm welcome.

In Norway, a three-pronged candle is placed atop the Yule tree, the three prongs representing the Wise Men. To the people of this country, it is important to leave a candle burning all night on Christmas Eve, for two reasons. First, it is a sign to weary travelers that they are welcome to stop here for rest and food. Second, it is considered that a light will keep away evil spirits! To avoid all chances of undesirable visitors on this holy night, some people used to take the extra precaution of leaving a candle burning on the hearth with salt sprinkled thickly around it.

In Denmark it is considered bad luck to touch the Yule candles with one's hands. The tapers on the tree and other Christmas candles are traditionally lighted by the mother of the family.

In Yugoslavia as in Norway, Christmas candles were thought to have the power to dispel evil spirits. There was an ancient superstition that the souls of the dead were wandering about on Christmas Eve. To guide them on their way, candles were placed in the windows of the homes and often one also on either side of the front door.

In Serbia, on Christmas Eve there used to be a custom among the farmers of hanging a box of wheat in a corner of the kitchen with a tall wax candle in the center. As soon as darkness had fallen, the father of the household would light the candle and lead the family in this prayer: "May there be a good yield of wheat, many new calves and lambs, and an abundance of milk and honey through the year about to begin!"

FIRES OF YULETIDE

Before the time of Christianity, it was customary to celebrate pagan holidays with great bonfires. One of the earliest legends concerning fire is the Norse tale of Hertha. She was the goddess of the hearth or home-fire. When a great fire had been laid on a platform of stones in preparation for a feast, with all the people gathered round it, Hertha, it was said, descended through the smoke. She was a kind goddess and it was thought that her appearance helped the fortunetellers to foretell the future. When chimneys were built into the houses, the people still looked for Hertha to come down the chimney. This probably is the origin of the Santa Claus legend which has him entering the homes through the chimney.

In the Christian era, the custom of lighting fires to celebrate holidays persisted in some places. In Finland an unusual custom at Christmas is called "paving the way" for the Christ Child. Great pine boughs are cut from the trees and piled up to make a huge green carpet. Then the people light pinewood torches called "good-luck chips" and form a procession. They carry their burning brands along the route of the "way" from the top of the hill down to the village square. If the lights burn well it means that the Christ Child will find His way.

A ceremony is held in Christian households in the land of Syria on Christmas Eve. Members of the family and their servants gather in the courtyard of the house. All hold lighted candles and one of the children reads the Nativity story. A fire is made of dried thorns and while it is burning a psalm is sung. Then each person jumps over the ashes of the fire three times and makes a wish. In the Christian churches a similar fire of thorns is built on Christmas Day and traditional hymns are chanted while it burns. These fires are said to be in honor of the Wise Men, to warm them on their journey to the holy manger.

In China, Christians used to usher in their Christmas holiday with a wonderful display of fireworks.

In our own country until recent times, the people in the South welcomed Christmas by shooting off fireworks, especially those that made a good loud noise. This custom was brought to Louisiana from France many years ago and spread to other Southern states. Some states and most large cities ban the sale and use of fireworks now, but in some rural sections the people still "shoot in" Christmas the old way.

THE YULE LOG

The Yule log came to England from the Norse custom of burning the *Juul* in honor of Thor. In Christian times this was adopted for the Christmas celebration. Burning the Yule log was a very important ceremony in the northern countries of Europe where it lent itself to the actual name for Christmas. Scandinavians call the Christmas season Yule and the Lithuanian word for Christmas literally means "log evening." The burning of the huge log was welcomed in the homes not only for its warmth, but also for the light it gave in the central room of the house. In early days even candles were scarce, and it can be imagined that the great fire must have lent considerable cheer to the festivities of Christmas. Many superstitions grew up in connection with its burning. There was a belief that the log must not be allowed to burn out during the twelve days of Christmas. Each year a piece was saved to set fire to the Yule log the following year. It was customary, too, to save some of the ashes. Some believed that the ashes had healing powers to cure the diseases of men and cattle. The Albanians scattered them over the fields, believing the ground would then yield better crops.

Bringing in the Yule log was attended with much ceremony. In Merrie England the log was chosen months before Christmas. On Christmas Eve it was dragged into the great hall of the house to the central fireplace with much merriment. The poet, Robert Herrick, wrote a song for the occasion:

> *Come bring with a noise,*
> *My merry, merry boys,*
> > *The Christmas Log to the firing;*
> *While my good dame she*
> *Bids ye all be free,*
> > *And drink to your heart's desiring.*

In some sections of Germany years ago, the piece of Yule log that remained after the holidays was brought back to the fireplace whenever a clap of thunder was heard, for it was believed that its burning would protect the house from being struck by lightning.

In Italy it was customary to pour a cup of wine over the burning log. In France the ashes of the *Suche* were used in rural places as a cure-all for various maladies, including chilblains. In Greece, young people told their fortunes by placing two olive leaves on the hot ashes of the Christmas log. In Bulgaria, a coin was hidden in the ashes to bring prosperity to the house. In Serbia, there was much importance given to the rituals connected with the *Badnyak*. First of all, the tree for the Yule log must fall to the east when it was hewn to assure good luck during the coming year. When the huge log was brought into the house the mother wished it a happy *"Badnyi Dan!"* and tossed a handful of wheat over it. The fire was tended very carefully through the night, for it was considered bad luck to let it go out. And when the burning log was struck hard with a shovel, it was fortunate if many, many sparks flew, for then there would be many baby calves, lambs, kids and piglings born on that farm.

And so we see how, through the past and the present, the lights of Christmas shine forth across the Christian world: the Star of Bethlehem appearing to proclaim the birth of a King; the candles gleaming in a million different places to light the way of the Holy Child; and the fires burning to shed light over the world, bringing warmth and cheer to the hearts of all who observe Christ's birthday.

CHRISTMAS GREENS

With holly and ivy
So green and so gay,
We deck up our houses
As fresh as the day.

When these lines were written in 1695, greens had been used as decorations for centuries. One of the customs of the old Roman Saturnalia was the decorating of houses and public places with evergreens. In those ancient times, green branches were used not so much for their beauty as for what they represented. Laurel, for example, symbolized peace, joy and victory. The Druid priests of Ancient Gaul and Britain used mistletoe in all their religious ceremonies because it was considered a sacred plant. The holly plant also was held sacred by them. When the people followed their Druid priests to the forests to cut the hallowed mistletoe, they usually wore a sprig of holly on their clothing. It was thought to protect them from evil forces and consequently they would be less likely to err in cutting the mistletoe. The Druids used the utmost care in this operation, for if the sacred plant should touch the ground it would lose its magic powers. They held a pure white cloth beneath the plant to catch it as it fell from the branches. The mistletoe, they thought, came from heaven because it needed no roots in the ground to make it grow. The people even considered sacred the great oak trees upon which the parasite mistletoe grew.

Mistletoe was considered an "all-healer" in diseases of man and beast. Among the Romans it was thought to be so much a symbol of peace that it was said even battles ceased momentarily when the enemy happened to meet under some mistletoe-laden oak. Even in modern times there are few places in Europe where some superstition concerning its healing power cannot be found among the people. In some parts of Italy it is even considered a charm to extinguish fire. Peasants of southern France use it to brew tea for stomach-ache. In England and America, the bit of mistletoe hung above the door at Christmas is said to bring good luck to the house. Best known is the custom of the kiss bestowed upon the maiden, young or old, who stands beneath it. Those who take advantage of this privilege are following the ancient Britons, for it was they who started it. When these ancients hung a sprig of the plant above their doors to ward off witches, it was customary for all who entered to receive a kiss.

At first the Christian Church frowned upon the use of mistletoe in the churches because it had been used by pagans in their religious rites. They considered it a heathenish and profane plant, and even today it is not generally used in the church. Other evergreens, however, have been used to deck the churches of England for the Christmas season. For centuries the English have made use of ivy, yew, box, laurel, rosemary, cypress and holly. Holly was always the favorite. This plant's name comes from the Anglo-Savon word *holen*. Perhaps the fact that it was used so profusely may have given the color scheme of red and green to the Christmas season. In Merrie England of the olden days it was put to many uses, even to trimming the beehives.

English people usually take down their Christmas greens on Twelfth Night, January sixth. For many years it was considered very bad luck to leave them in the house after Candlemas Day, February second. Some said that the leaves still remaining on the greens left hanging indoors stood for ghosts and goblins one might expect to see in that house! An old rhyme goes:

> *Not one least branch left there behind,*
> *For look how many leaves there be*
> *Neglected there (maids trust to me)*
> *So many goblins shall ye see!*

The French people decorate their churches with greens, but fresh flowers are also used at the altar, with many lighted candles to lend color to the Noël scene.

In Norway, besides the evergreen branches in this land of many trees, the blue berries from the juniper and the red clusters from the mountain ash are used for decorations. The people of Finland are not given to decorating with evergreens because they consider them a symbol of mourning. Instead, they use straw to cover the floor to simulate the lowly stable wherein the Holy Babe was born.

In those countries where Christmas comes during the hot weather, flowers take the place of evergreens. In Australia, huge ferns and palm leaves are used with fresh flowers. Two beautiful Christmas plants bloom there in time for the decorations. These are the Christmas Bell, so-called because of the red bell-shaped flower, and the Christmas Bush, which consists of tiny red flowers growing in close clusters. In Mexico, flowers are sold very cheap in the market stalls, among them the scarlet *Noche Bueno*. Here, also, is the beautiful Flame Leaf, or poinsettia as we know it. This plant as it grows in Mexico, to a height of ten feet, is breathtaking.

The poinsettia was introduced to America many years ago by our first minister to Mexico, Dr. Joel Robert Poinsett. In 1828 Dr. Poinsett sent some cuttings of the Flame Leaf to friends in America. The unusual plant was named in his honor and is today the most popular of all Christmas flowers. Most of those sold at Christmas are shipped from the southern part of California. At San Diego, which has become the poinsettia center of the world, there is a Poinsettia Fiesta held every year at Christmas.

In America, as soon as the Christmas trees come on the market, greens for decorating can be bought from the same merchants who sell the trees. Laurel strung in ropes is a favorite for outdoor decorating and for large halls and gymnasiums where Christmas entertainments or dances are held. Holly is another favorite. Aside from these there are fir and pine boughs, mistletoe, eucalyptus, cedar, boxwood, ivy and cones from the pines. Each home decorator has his own special way of using the greens to best advantage. A clever decorator makes use of greens cut from the garden or from a too-high Christmas tree. These can be brightened with the addition of bright berries or fruits such as apples, crabapples, oranges, or even cranberries strung like popcorn. Some fasten small Christmas tree balls to their green boughs. The effects depend upon the ingenuity of the one doing the trimming.

When we trim our houses with evergreens or flowers we never stop to consider that the custom is centuries old. In some sections of Europe, too, there are ways of decorating that are likewise taken for granted. However, if we were to go into some of these houses at the Christmas season we probably would consider their customs strange. In Serbia and Poland, for instance, straw is a "must" in preparing the house for Yule. In Poland the straw is scattered upon the table where the Christmas Eve supper will be set. In Serbia, straw is brought into the house on the eve of Yule and scattered generously about the kitchen and into the corners of the other rooms. One Serbian writer tells how the children followed his mother about the house as she scattered the straw. They pretended they were little chickens following after her, the mother hen, as she imitated the clucking of a hen. After these rituals were over and the father had asked the blessing, the family sat upon the floor to eat the Christmas Eve feast! A cloth was laid over the straw and all the dishes of good things placed upon it. Although this may sound like a winter picnic, the significance was to remind the keepers of Christ's birthday that the Lord was born in a lowly manger with straw for His bed. Straw was used by the people of Finland also. On Christmas Eve they scattered it on the floor in the room where the family ate their Yuletide feast. In some places a sort of canopy was built over the room to simulate a sky. It was fashioned of straw and often decorated with paper stars.

In Italy, an unusual form of decoration is known as the *ceppo*. In many places this has been replaced by the modern Christmas tree. Originally the *ceppo* was a log that was kept burning throughout the days of Christmas. About a century ago this became, instead of the flaming log, an object of decoration. Families vied with one another in fashioning their *ceppo* just as people do today in creating the Christmas crèche. Actually, as time went on, the *ceppo* resembled a crèche to some extent. The shape was somewhat like a Christmas tree. It had three or four shelves, each shelf smaller than the one beneath it. The bottom shelf usually held a replica of the Nativity scene with the figures of the Holy Family, the shepherds and the Wise Men. The remainder of the shelves contained small gifts for the children of the family, as well as sweetmeats and fruits. The *ceppo* could be as fancy as the owner wished to make it. It was often decorated with bright-colored papers and tinsel and flags, and always with lighted candles.

Most beloved of all the Christmas greens, of course, is the Christmas tree. It is not known exactly when an evergreen tree was first brought into the home and set up and trimmed, and made the main feature of the decorating scheme for Christmas. There are many stories and legends connected with its origin, some of which you will find in this book. The Germans are probably the first nation to have made the tree the center of the Christmas celebration. We are told that Martin Luther was first to bring a fir tree into the house and set lighted tapers on it for his children.

The custom of trimming trees goes back many centuries. The ancient Romans often hung masks of Bacchus on the branches of their fruit trees, believing that this would cause them to bear more fruit. One of the earliest references to trimming Christmas trees is from an English book dated 1444. This tells of a Christmas tree being set up in the "pavement" of a village and being trimmed with ivy and other greens. Trinkets or ornaments were not mentioned. The next reference to a "trimmed" tree appeared in 1604. This is an account of how the people of Strasbourg in Alsace, while still under German rule, trimmed some fir trees which they brought into their homes for Christmas. They used paper roses and gold foil, apples and sweets to trim the branches.

The custom of the Christmas tree spread through Germany and became dear to German-speaking people everywhere. It spread gradually to other countries of Europe, including Austria, France and the Scandinavian countries, and finally to England and then America.

Although there are records of the appearance of Christmas trees in England in the early eighteen hundreds, it was the royal family at Windsor Castle that made the custom popular there. Queen Victoria's husband, Prince Albert, was a native of Saxe-Coburg where Christmas trees were an important feature of Christmas. In 1840, after their first son was born, Prince Albert had a fir tree brought into the parlor, where he trimmed it with tapers, pretty baubles and an angel at the top. Since then the illuminated

Christmas tree has been a favorite custom with the English. In some places in England the "living Christmas tree" is preferred. The tree is taken up from the soil and planted in a tub, then kept damp throughout the holidays and later replanted when the soil is warm enough.

In Germany it used to be customary in some families to have an individual tree for each member of the family, with the Christmas gifts arranged beneath it. It must have taken much time and many decorations to deck so many trees, but the people loved this part of Christmas. They used a great deal of tinsel on their trees, and also wax tapers and numerous small toys and dolls, and gilded nuts and sweetmeats. *Lubecker marzipan* is still a favorite candy for trimming the tree. Marzipan is also popular with French children at Christmas. It is a sweet candy made in the shape of meats and fruits and vegetables.

In Norway, gilded nuts have always been popular as a tree-trimming. Years ago the Scandinavians, always great fishermen, used fish nets to deck the Yule tree, and sometimes tiny flags. Today the tree ornaments of the Norwegians are mostly delicious, edible trimmings, such as special cookies made in the shape of animals, and nuts, apples and candies. Lighted candles grace the branches and on top there is a large three-pronged candle symbolizing the three Wise Men.

The people of Poland began years ago to trim their tree with ribbons and gaily colored paper ornaments. Today they use more modern decorations but their tree is still lavishly trimmed and is often so large it takes up a whole room.

In Lithuania the people used birdcages made of straw to trim their tree. But in India where the Christian missions celebrate Christ's birth there is the strangest tree of all! A banana tree substitutes for the missing evergreen tree. It is a strange sight with the bananas still growing on it and the bright tree ornaments and numerous gift packages supplementing the yellow fruit! To the children waiting for gifts, it is a beautiful and wonderful tree!

In Hawaii, many of the Christmas trees are sprayed with white paint to make them look snow-laden.

The Christmas tree is thought to have been introduced to our colonies during the American Revolution by the professional Hessian soldiers sent here by England. As a custom, however, it was not adopted until much later. At first there were some who were against bringing the evergreen tree into the church. But gradually the opposition turned to approval, and a Christmas tree became an accepted and welcome sight at every Sunday school Christmas entertainment. Like the tree set up by Prince Albert at Windsor Castle, the one displayed at the White House by President Franklin Pierce and Mrs. Pierce during his administration probably did much to popularize the custom in the United States. By the twentieth century a Christmas tree was a part of every Christmas celebration in America.

Years ago the ornaments of a Christmas tree were quite different from those of today. The majority were homemade. There were strings of popcorn, brightly painted walnuts, paper chains made in bright colors, and other ornaments often fashioned by the eager fingers of the children in the family. There were tiny wax candles in little tin holders to grace the tips of every branch, and yards of bright tinsel to drape the green boughs, to say nothing of the lovely paper angel with cotton wings that looked down from the topmost branch. There were tiny toys and candy canes, too, and marzipan made in the shape of fruits and vegetables to tempt the appetites of boys and girls who could reach high enough to sample them. Today the many trinkets and baubles have almost disappeared. There are, instead, store-bought trimmings of beautiful colored glass with hosts of colored electric lights. Our Christmas tree today is often breath-taking in beauty, but perhaps not so interesting as the old-fashioned ornament-laden tree.

With the demand for trees growing each year, the Christmas tree industry has thrived. At one time it was feared that the tremendous sale of young evergreens cut from the forests annually would deplete the country's forests. But quite the reverse is true. Almost all Christmas trees are grown in controlled forests or on Christmas tree farms and are cut by experts who know that if it is done correctly the growth of the forests will be helped. The trees are cut while young from dense portions of the woods, which solves the thinning problem. In spite of all the millions of trees cut each year, the supplies increase rather than diminish. Spruce and fir, and yellow and white pine are the favorites. Cedar and cypress, juniper and hemlock also are used by the hundreds of thousands to meet the demand for "a pretty Christmas tree."

On Christmas Day of 1925 the famous General Grant tree, a giant sequoia in the General Grant National Park, near Sanger, California, was designated as the Nation's Christmas Tree. The tree is 267 feet high and has a circumference of 107 feet. This magnificent tree has reached the awe-inspiring age of three thousand, five hundred years and seems a worthy choice for our national Christmas tree.

"A mile of Christmas trees" can be seen on our West Coast in Altadena, California. In 1882 a Californian, Frederick J. Woodbury, brought back some deodar seeds from India where he had been traveling, because he thought the deodar cedar trees of India so beautiful. He hopefully planted the seeds on his property and his hopes were realized. Three years later the young trees were transplanted into a double row, forming a lane to the ranch. This was long ago, and today the lane formed by the two hundred huge deodar trees is a famous street in Altadena. Each year during Christmas week, the avenue at night becomes a long brilliant lane of illuminated Christmas trees, the great branches of the cedars aflame with thousands of colored lights. Millions of visitors in cars with their lights dimmed have traveled slowly down the awesome Mile of Christmas Trees.

Two other special Christmas trees are visited by throngs of people annually. The first is the tree at the nation's capital in Washington, which is always lit ceremoniously by the president. The other is the great tree at Rockefeller Center in New York City. This tree, always impressively beautiful, is estimated to have had more visitors each year than any other Christmas tree in the world. One of the great attractions is the carol-singing beside it, led by the Radio Center Choristers.

The community Christmas tree set up in "the square"for everybody to enjoy is seen in thousands of great cities and small towns all over our country. This traditional custom is one of the finest ways of all to spread peace and good will and fellowship at the season of Christ's birth.

When the German people trimmed their first Christmas tree so long ago, placing stars and lighted tapers and angels on it, a wonderful custom began. As we enjoy our own Christmas tree let us join our thoughts with our neighbors all across the world and with them sing: "O Tannenbaum! O Tannenbaum!"

THE CHRISTMAS FEAST

Since ancient times when grain was first grown and harvested, bread has been known as the staff of life. Long before the time of Christ the Hebrews gave thanks to God for the bread upon their table. The ancient Scandinavian people held a festival known as Yule, which is now the Scandinavian Christmas, and a boar's head at the family feast honored the "Sun-boar." Pre-Christian Romans called their festival Saturnalia. It was customary at this time to give small presents to the Roman senators. The most popular gifts were sweet cakes, and these are thought to be the ancestors of our Christmas cookies. Thus we can see how some of our Christmas foods of today are relics of times even before Christ's birth.

It was natural that Christmas doughs and breads should attain great meaning at the Christmas feast, especially in the Middle Ages when times were hard and bread was indeed the staff of life. Perhaps it was during this period that the legend of the Dough and the Christ Child began to be told.

It was said to have happened when the Holy Family was fleeing from the wicked Herod's soldiers. As the soldiers gained upon Joseph and Mary and the Child, they sought refuge in the home of a woman busy with the making of the family bread. "Quickly, hide Him!" cried Mary, and thrust her Babe into the woman's doughy hands. The soldiers at that moment knocked upon the woman's door. With no time to hesitate, the goodwife quickly dropped the Babe into her great mass of dough, and went on kneading. When the soldiers entered stomping and shouting and accused her of hiding the Child, she kept her head bent quietly over the bread mixture, kneading, thumping, slapping at the dough. Mary and Joseph stood by trembling in fear that such rough treatment would set their Son to crying out. But the little Lord Jesus made not a sound, and soon the soldiers wearied of their search and went on to the next house. The Christ Child was safe!

When Mary had lifted her little Son from the bread dough a strange thing happened. The bread kept rising higher and higher, and was light as a feather. No matter how much of it the woman put into the oven there was always some left. The neighbors, and then folks from far and near, came to get a piece of the magical rising to bake with their bread. And thus it continued from that day to this, a small portion of each dough being saved for the next rising.

In some sections of Rumania a ritual is performed with the dough of the popular *turté*. On the day before Christmas Eve the mother prepares the dough for these delicious sweet cakes. While her fingers are covered with dough she walks out to the orchard where her husband is standing poised ready to cut down a fruit tree. She tells him he must not cut down the tree because

[93]

she is sure that "it will be as full of fruit as my fingers are now full of dough." The father relents, and they go on to the next tree. They repeat this performance at each tree, the man seemingly determined to chop down the tree, the mother coaxing him to save it.

As we learn more about the Christmas foods of the world, we shall see that breads and doughs and cakes are used in some form by all nations.

In England it is considered important by some families to eat twelve pies (usually meat or mince pies) between the days of Christmas and Epiphany, to bring good luck in all twelve months of the year to follow.

In olden days the bakers featured Yule Doughs made in the images of the Babe and Madonna. These were presented as gifts to their customers. A Christmas pie in those days contained many ingredients. An old book called Hone's Table Book lists them as follows: 4 geese, 2 turkeys, 4 wild ducks, 2 rabbits, 2 curlews, 7 blackbirds, 6 pigeons, 4 partridges, 6 snipe, 2 woodcocks, 2 neats' tongues, 2 bushels of flour and 20 pounds of butter!

Originally mince pies were called mutton pies. They were baked in the form of a manger and many of them had a tiny image of the Holy Babe on the top crust. After the manger-shape of the pie was no longer popular, mince pies were rectangular and finally, as today, were baked in the popular round pie tins.

A popular dish of old England was the boar's head, about which much has been written in story and verse. In the great houses of this period when much entertaining was done, the boar's head was carried in to the Christmas feast by the chief cook on a gold or silver platter. He was always followed by a whole retinue of other servants, while the guests sang the Boar's Head Carol:

> *The boar's head in hand bring I*
> *With garlands gay and rosemary;*
> *I pray you all sing merrily,*
> *Quot estis in convivio.*

But this dish was only one of the more than plenty that were served, course after course, at the Christmas feast! Historians tell us that Christmas dinners were known to last for nine hours at a sitting! Let us take a look at a menu of one such feast held some time in the fifteen hundreds. Included were: Roast boar's head, roasts of beef, beef tongue, and venison; a boiled capon, a boiled beef, a roasted goose, a roasted swan, and a whole roasted pig; roast turkey and mince pie; a venison pasty and a kid with a pudding in the belly; a roasted capon with olive pie; custards, salads, fricassees, sweets and pastries of several kinds; celery, carrots, parsnips and turnips; and of course, bread, wines and ales.

It is said that one of Queen Elizabeth the First's Christmas dinners was well-nigh spoiled for her because the peacock was borne to the table upon a silver platter instead of a golden dish as she had ordered!

There is a legend about the origin of the famous English plum pudding. It is said that an early English king was lost in a blizzard while on a hunting trip on the day before Christmas. In order to make as fine a holiday dish as possible with what he had, his cook is said to have put everything edible into the making of a pudding. This contained chopped deer meat, flour, spices, plums, apples, and plenty of brandy and sugar. And out came the first plum pudding!

"Wassail" is derived from the Saxon expression *Was Haile,* meaning "your health." The wassail bowl was the favorite Christmas drink in England for centuries. It was always drunk with much ceremony and exchanging of greetings for Christmas and the New Year. The custom was so common to all classes of people at the Christmas feast that "wassailing" came to mean any kind of Christmas toasting. Today the old wassail bowl recipe has been replaced by a more popular punch. And today in England instead of boar's head and peacock pie on the Christmas table there are the popular roast goose, capon or turkey with mince pie, and plum pudding.

[95]

In Scotland one member of the family had to be out of bed early to bake the bannocks which were always eaten Christmas morning. It was said to be unlucky if these cakes "broke" in the oven.

The French housewife bakes a special Christmas cookie containing whole wheat flour, brown sugar and dates. Some people think it will bring bad luck if a portion of the Christmas Cake is not shared with some needy person first. The Noël Eve feast is served after midnight mass. The hostess uses her best china and silver and sets the table with flowers and candles, for this is a very special meal. On Twelfth Night the bakers give *galettes*, a flaky pastry with a bean baked in each, to their customers. The one who finds the bean will be "king" or "queen" of the feast.

In Belgium, if the children are good a bun called Angel's Cake will be found under their pillows in the morning. As in France, on the Eve of Epiphany a King's Cake containing a bean is served to determine who shall be king of the feast. Sometimes a small china doll is used in place of the bean.

Cakes baked in the shapes of animals and birds and St. Nicholas are popular in Holland. The St. Nicholas cakes are served everywhere in that country on December sixth, St. Nicholas Day. If there is a fog on that morning the children are told it is smoke rising from the ovens of the good saint as he bakes his cakes!

The Germans are noted for their delicious Christmas cookies and the housewives take great pains in their preparation. So many cookies are baked that the job of stirring the dough is a serious matter. Almost every community has its own favorite kind of Christmas cake or cookie. In Saxony, for instance, the long narrow cookies called *Stollen* are most popular. Full of currants and sprinkled with sugar, these were originally shaped like a manger in honor of the Christ Child's crib. In the city of Hamburg, spice and honey and gingerbread cookies are the favorites. In some places there are the delicious Christmas loaves called "Christstollen" bursting their crispy crusts with fruit and citron and nuts.

The Christmas Eve feast starts in Sweden with a *smörgåsbord.* This is a separate table laden with a great variety of good things prepared as only the Swedish can prepare them. Everyone helps himself from the many dishes on this table and then sits down to a meal of roast goose or perhaps roast pork, and lutfisk, and ends with *Julgrôt,* the rich Christmas rice pudding. Lutfisk is a national favorite. Weeks before Christmas the largest and best fish of the catch is chosen, and blessed by the priest. It is dried, then soaked in a special solution that swells it to nearly four times its normal size. When it appears on the Yule table it is a tender delicacy like no other food. In Norway the people eat rice pudding with an almond in it. The one who finds the almond will be first to be married! The little elves (*Julenisser*) are always given a bowl of pudding by the children before they go to bed. In Denmark thousands of tiny cookies called peppernuts are baked to last throughout the Christmas season. It is considered bad luck if a visitor to the house goes away without tasting the holiday cakes. In Finland the traditional rice pudding is known as St. Stephen's Porridge. It is eaten on Christmas Day, which is the day before St. Stephen's.

Magi cakes are very popular in Italy. They are eaten on Magi Day (Epiphany) and also on Christmas Day. Some of the foods of the Italian Christmas feast, such as larks and eels, would seem strange to us. The eels are always bought while alive. Prepared, they are called *capitoni* and are a great delicacy. Sparkling burgundy wine is served before and after the Christmas feast.

In Spain truffled turkey is a favorite for Christmas, and sea bream is considered a great delicacy. The Spanish people are very fond of sweets and rich preserves. Cakes are offered as gifts among families and friends and some families will serve these in many varieties to end the Christmas feast.

A Christmas almond paste is mixed by the Portuguese housewives and made into delicious cookies. These are offered with wine to the carolers who come by on Epiphany.

In Switzerland honey-pastries in such forms as animals, birds and angels are baked and hung on the tree. The children enjoy these when the time comes to dismantle the Christmas tree.

Cookies, or thin wafers, are baked by the hundreds in Poland and blessed by the priests. These, called *oplatki,* are stamped with the figures of the Nativity scene. On Christmas Eve when the first star appears in the sky, the *oplatki* are broken by each member of the family and offered to another while Christmas greetings are exchanged. These wafers also are given, with Christmas greetings, to friends and relatives much as we exchange Christmas cards. In Poland an extra place is set at the table "for the Christ Child." It is considered lucky if some needy person knocks at the door when it is time to serve the Christmas supper, and he is given the extra seat at the table.

In old Russia the Christmas Eve meal, which broke the fast preceding Christmas, was started by the breaking of "the blessed wafer." Each person received a portion of this, after which a feast generally featuring roast pig was enjoyed. The Ukrainians broke their fast with a wonderful repast containing twelve different dishes, each dish representing one of the apostles. The traditional dish to begin this feast was the *kutia,* a porridge made with wheat and honey.

The Hungarians are very fond of poppy seeds. They have always used them generously at Christmas time in their cookies and cakes. On Christmas Eve they eat fish and dumplings that contain poppy seeds. The Bulgarians have a favorite Christmas cake called the *kravai.* This large round cake is gaily decorated and then given the center of the table with the other foods arranged around it. In Czechoslovakia the Christmas Eve meal always has seven courses, ending with generous samples of the numerous kinds of Christmas cookies. Rumanian Christmas cakes are made of dough that is given a special twist before baking. This is supposed to make it resemble the swaddling clothes of the infant Jesus. The Serbian Christmas *zhito* cake contains a coin to bring good luck to the one who finds it in his serving. Roast pig is the traditional main course of the Serbian Christmas dinner. Years ago contests were held in the village to see whose pig was first ready to serve. It was the custom to shoot off a pistol when the roast was done, announcing the winners to all the others.

In Latvia, the people like to serve delicious small meat-filled pastries at their Christmas Eve supper. Lithuanians also eat these, and end their meal with thin wafers called *plotkeles.*

The Albanians carry out the custom of eating unleavened bread on Christmas Day in honor of the food that Mary and Joseph, as Jews, ate on special days.

Greek housewives make hundreds of *tegenites* to appease appetites over the holidays. These are fried bread made in fancy shapes. When the carolers go from house to house on Christmas morning they are given *tegenites* and nuts and fruit, and they call these the "Luck of Christ." In some Greek churches plates of this food are placed before the figure of Mary, the Mother of Christ.

The people of South America often enjoy their Christmas dinner out-of-doors since it is their hot season. In some places roasted peacock is the main course, but more often it is roast pork. Everyone eats *buñuelos* during the holidays. These are delicate pancakes eaten with honey. In Venezuela a meat pie is baked with corn meal and eaten as the main course at the Christmas feast.

A special salad accompanies other delicious dishes on a Mexican table on Christmas Eve. It is made of fresh fruits and vegetables and garnished with pretty colored candies. It was in Mexico that turkeys were first raised for their meat by the Aztec Indians hundreds of years ago. Tortillas and fried peppers are served with the turkey. On Epiphany a cake is baked in the shape of a crown with a tiny doll hidden in it. This cake, *rosca de reyes,* is important to the guests of an Epiphany dinner because the one who finds the doll is obligated to give a party on Candlemas Day. At that time the figure of the Christ Child is ceremoniously removed from the Christmas *nacimiento* or crèche. Many cookies are baked for Christmas; the most popular contain ajonjolí seeds.

Everyone who reads this book is familiar with the Christmas foods of our own country. There are turkey with dressing and cranberry sauce, mashed potatoes and turnips, vegetables and salads, topped off with mince and pumpkin pies; to say nothing of certain family favorites that some families wouldn't dream of omitting from the feast! Homemade cakes and cookies and crullers, and candies with stuffed dates, plum puddings and fruit cake help to make Christmas and the days that follow ones of endless feasting.

Christmas cookies are a specialty in the homes of almost every American family, but especially among the Moravians of Pennsylvania who prepare them far ahead of the season in great quantities. The names of these are straight from the German ancestors where the recipes originated: *Lebkuchen* (ginger cakes), *Pfeffernusse* (spice-and-nut cookies), *Springerle, Belsnickel* cakes, and *Leckerli*, a word meaning delicious morsel! Samples of the various cookies are exchanged among families and friends, some in fancy shapes are hung on the Christmas tree or placed in the *putz* (crèche), and plates of them are offered to visitors to the house during the holidays.

As early as President Washington's time the Southern people took great pride in preparing and serving a wonderful Christmas dinner. A famous Christmas recipe is Martha Washington's own Christmas Cake which called for forty eggs, among other fabulous ingredients.

In every part of the United States there can be found special Christmas dishes which have been adopted from the forbears of the particular family who prepares them. Thus we find that with few exceptions all of our traditional holiday foods have come from other countries. To be sure, we have our purely American turkey, our corn pudding and corn pone, and our delicious cranberry sauce and pumpkin pie! For all the good things that grace our tables on Christmas Day, we are grateful not only to our pioneer Americans but to our millions of newer Americans who have brought to this country their special holiday fare.

THE ANIMALS OF CHRISTMAS

What part do animals play in the Christmas celebration? When we place the figures of little donkeys and miniature cows and sheep and lambs in our crèche, we are honoring those humble beasts who were close to Jesus at His birth, sharing their lowly stable with Him. From the earliest years of Christianity, countless stories and legends have been told of the roles played by animals and birds and bees in the Nativity.

One old legend tells us that the barnyard animals show their adoration of the Christ Child by falling to their knees just at midnight on Christmas Eve. This story came to our own country through the early settlers from Germany and Switzerland. When the American Indians learned of the Baby Jesus, they had their own interpretation in their belief that the deer knelt at midnight on Christmas Eve. Another belief in the rural sections of European countries was that the barnyard animals were given the power of speech at midnight to announce Christ's birthday to the world. It was conceded, however, that human beings should never try to listen for this event lest misfortune befall the eavesdropper.

The people of Norway so honor all animals for their connection with the holy birth that special treatment is bestowed upon them at Yuletide. Cattle, birds and even fish are assured of safety during this time which has always been called the Peace of Christmas. For generations it has been the custom to set no snares during this period. Even the fishnets that earned the daily bread were taken in so that the fish might swim the waters in peace. Cattle were well fed and the birds given feasts of suet. Sometimes the farmers fed their cows salt from a cow-bell, so that they would be able to find their way home at night without straying.

In Spain, the cows are given special treatment on *Noche Buena,* the people say, because the little Jesus was kept warm on the night of His birth when the cattle breathed upon Him. In Scotland, the farmers see to it that all the animals receive some extra rations on Christmas Day. In Yugoslavia, too, this custom is kept to reward the beasts' faithful service throughout the year. In days gone by it was not unusual for some members of the family to sleep in the barn with the animals in order to make room in the house for the many guests.

In old Italy on Christmas Eve a curious ceremony often took place in the farmer's barn. The farmer and his shepherd would carry lighted candles into every corner of the animals' shelter, holding the tapers high so that light was shed into every dark corner.

Lambs are well represented in the Christmas scene because of the part played by the shepherds in the Nativity. In Belgium, one may see a little white lamb being led by a small boy who represents John the Baptist, in a religious procession. In southern France it used to be customary for the shepherd of a flock to bring one new-born lamb to the church on Christmas Eve to be blessed by the priest. This custom is still carried out in a ceremony held at midnight mass in Les Baux, France. Men and women dressed as shepherds and shepherdesses form a procession to the church. Following them, a white lamb is conveyed to the church in a chariot that is pulled by a ram.

Birds have always been featured in Christmas legends. In Scandinavian literature there is a story of Jesus as a boy helping His playmates to make clay birds. When Jesus had finished modeling His clay bird, the story relates, He would clap His hands and the little bird would come to life, flying joyfully off into the skies. Perhaps this is one reason why the Scandinavians are so good to birds, remembering to feed them when the ground is snow-covered. Even before they partake of their own Christmas Eve repast the farmers of Norway, Sweden and Denmark give the birds their Yuletide supper. First they erect a pole in the yard or on the roof of the barn. If possible, they see to it that a few branches remain on the very top of the evergreen pole, so that the birds can settle on these branches after they have eaten their Christmas meal. They place a large sheaf of grain at the top. This may be wheat, barley, or oats, but it is always the nicest sheaf saved by the farmer at threshing time. This is a common practice among our own Scandinavian-Americans of Minnesota, Wisconsin, Illinois and North Dakota.

In Ireland, the little wren is called "king of the birds" because of a legend that told how he had flown higher than any other bird. In a contest to see which could fly higher, an eagle competed with a skylark. But unnoticed by the two contestants, the little wren perched himself on the back of the eagle and was born aloft in the flight. The skylark finally could fly no higher, and both thought that the eagle was the winner. But when that great bird started to descend, the wren left his perch on the eagle's back and flew higher. "You see," he called down to the eagle and the sky-lark, "I am flying high above you. I am King of the Birds!" And so in Ireland a strange custom came into being on St. Stephen's Day, the day after Christmas. A group of boys place a wren in a cage. Then they carry the cage on top of a branch and go about singing the story of the wren. The song starts like this:

The wren, the wren, the King of all Birds,
St. Stephen's Day, she caught in the furze (bush).
Although she is little, her family is great,
Cheer up, landlady, and give us a treat.

[103]

The "treat" was in the form of pennies which the boys saved up for a dance on New Year's Day.

A German legend tells how the fir trees saved a flock of wild canaries from destruction. It was on Christmas Eve in the Hartz Mountains of Germany, and a violent storm was raging. With terrific winds blowing, and heavy snow and sleet, it seemed as though the tiny winged creatures would surely be dashed to their death. The songs of the yellow canaries had turned into cries of hopelessness. Their calls of distress were apparently being swallowed up in the great roar and whine of the winds, but in spite of the din the little canaries were heard by the fir trees. "Stay with us; our branches will shelter you through the storm," they called out to the golden birds. And the little canaries were given refuge from the awful storm, and lived to sing the praises of their protectors. The legend goes that when the canaries now sing in their cages on Christmas Eve they are still singing praises to the firs who saved their ancestors, those canaries in the Hartz Mountains of northern Germany.

In some parts of Germany and in Switzerland, the farmer's wife makes the rounds of the hencoops on Christmas Eve to clip the chickens' wings. They say that if this is done it will protect the chickens against the beasts of prey that seem all the year round to be lying in wait for a nice meal of fowl. Perhaps clipping their wings keeps the chickens from flying away from the safety of the barnyard. In Belgium, the barnyard fowls are given oats that have been blessed for the same purpose. In the olden days in Russia one of the peasants' favorite pastimes on Christmas Eve was telling fortunes. Some used a hen for the purpose. The hen was brought into the house where five small heaps of chicken feed had been placed on the floor. Each small pile of grain was given a name: love, wealth, success, health or ill-fortune. The maiden whose future was being foretold would wait in breathless suspense to see from which pile the hen would choose to eat her Christmas supper. The hen's choice and what it symbolized was supposed to designate what the future would hold.

Even the little bee is not neglected in the legends of Christmas. Long ago in England it was believed that bees sang to the Christ Child at midnight on Christmas Eve. Because of this old belief, some beekeepers of England still place a bit of holly on the beehives.

Camels in the Christmas scene represent the camels the Wise Men rode in their travels to visit the new-born Child. Today in the Holy Lands the camel is a popular mode of transportation just as it was two thousand years ago. A Syrian story explains why little Syrian children believe a little camel brings their gifts on the day of Epiphany. It is said that when the Wise Men were seeking the Christ Child the camels grew very weary. When at last they had found the place where Jesus was, and the Wise Men came forward to present their gifts, the littlest camel fell to the ground in his great weariness. And so the Christ Child blessed the little camel and promised that thenceforth he would be able to carry gifts to children on this anniversary.

In some places, instead of camels, the horse is said to be the steed of the Wise Men. On the eve of *Dia de los Reyes,* or Day of the Kings, the boys and girls of Argentina never fail to leave hay and water for the horses of the Magi. And where do they leave it? Usually on the balcony, for these horses of the Kings are said to be able to leap through the air as miraculously as do Santa's reindeer. In those countries where St. Nicholas Day (December 6) is observed, the boys and girls put out hay and carrots for St. Nicholas's horse. In Belgium and Germany, St. Nicholas rides through the towns on a white horse or pony, distributing gifts to the children who have been good.

A Christmas goat or *Yul-bock* is familiar to the children of the Scandinavian countries. In Sweden, the children are told that the Yule ram will butt them if they are disobedient, but this doesn't seem to frighten them very much. They regard him with great affection. Displayed with the Christmas candles in these countries, you can usually see a small straw goat. In Norway they leave food out for the *Julebukk.* If he ignores it, it means that the ram has been offended in some way, and this is considered a bad omen. However, in most cases the boys and girls find the dish empty. But sometimes they find grain in the dish, and that will mean a good crop year is ahead. In some Norwegian homes the *Julebukk* actually comes into the living room for a surprise visit on Yule Eve with the *Julenisser* riding on his back. If there are naughty children present, the ram will try hard to butt them, all of this taking place amid screams of laughter. In Denmark, the *Klapper-bock* as they call him, usually consists of a pole which the rider straddles like a hobby-horse. A goat skin and a head fashioned of paper or wood make the animal realistic enough to cause lots of fun among the children.

A hobby-horse was used in the plays that were very popular in England years ago. These plays were given by traveling players and were especially welcomed at the Christmas season. In Wales, the strange animal character of the plays was called a Hodening Horse. He was very ugly and frightening to little children, especially when he peeked into the windows! However, after it was known that the horrible looking creature was only a Hodening Horse, he and the other characters were welcomed into the house and given a treat of cakes and cider.

In Old Russia, it used to be the custom at gatherings on Christmas Eve to masquerade as barnyard animals, representing the animals that were present at the birth of the Christ Child.

Most of the legends and beliefs about Christmas animals are very ancient. On the other hand, one animal that came into prominence later is the Christmas reindeer. It is difficult to determine exactly when he first made his appearance, or why. One story has it that the Christ Child told St. Nicholas he might choose any animal he wished to draw his gift-laden sleigh on Christmas Eve. But it was Santa Claus, and not St. Nicholas, with whom the legend of the reindeer grew up. At any rate, it was the poem written by Clement C. Moore in the year 1822 that fastened the reindeer to Santa's sleigh in unforgettable fashion, to the satisfaction of boys and girls by the millions. The words of the poem, "A Visit from St. Nicholas," tell the facts that no true believer in Santa Claus would dream of doubting:

> *The moon, on the breast of the new-fallen snow,*
> *Gave a lustre of midday to objects below;*
> *When what to my wondering eyes should appear,*
> *But a miniature sleigh and eight tiny reindeer,*
> *With a little old driver, so lively and quick*
> *I knew in a moment it must be St. Nick.*
> *More rapid than eagles his coursers they came,*
> *And he whistled and shouted and called them by name:*
> *"Now, Dasher! now, Dancer! now, Prancer and Vixen!*
> *On, Comet! on, Cupid! on, Donder and Blitzen!*
> *To the top of the porch, to the top of the wall!*
> *Now, dash away, dash away, dash away all!"*
> *As dry leaves that before the wild hurricane fly,*
> *When they meet with an obstacle, mount to the sky,*
> *So, up to the house-top the coursers they flew,*
> *With a sleigh full of toys—and St. Nicholas too.*

So we find many animals taking their unforgettable parts in the Christmas scene. The patient, faithful barnyard beasts who serve mankind so well are there. The camels and the horses and the goats play their parts. The birds, who were first in all the world to carol, and the bees who "sing" Christ's praises, are in the Christmas picture. The reindeer are there, too, and likely to remain. When we think of them all we feel certain that the little Lord Jesus would approve, for these are His own creatures every one.

THE GIFTS OF CHRISTMAS

One of the joys of Christmas is the exchange of gifts, a universal custom at this blessed season. How did the custom begin? We know that the Wise Men took gifts to Christ on His birthday, and some think of that as the beginning. Then there is Santa Claus, who was really St. Nicholas many years ago. St. Nicholas was noted for his generosity and his name became associated with surprise gift-giving. But there is still another possible explanation. Even before the Wise Men, and centuries before St. Nicholas, gift-giving on special occasions was popular. Let us try to explore all these clues to the answer to our question.

In ancient Roman times there was a custom of giving gifts of money at New Year's to those who were in authority. A box was placed in a prominent place in the town and the money was deposited therein. But the gifts came to include more than just money; food and clothing and even precious jewels were demanded and offered. Many years later, European and English monarchs grew accustomed to receiving gifts at the beginning of the New Year and then, later, at Christmas. In the time of Queen Elizabeth the First, every man gave to her of his wealth at Christmas according to his ability to pay. And it was said that almost her entire wardrobe consisted of clothing she had received as Christmas gifts.

This compulsory giving is not the sort we like to associate with Christmas. Let us, then, consider St. Nicholas.

In another part of this book we have told how St. Nicholas, because his saint day came in December, gradually became associated with Christmas Eve, and how his reputation spread to many lands as the bringer of gifts. However, in Holland, Belgium, parts of France and Germany the eve of his saint day is still celebrated as the time for gift-giving. In those places he is always shown dressed in his white bishop's robes, wearing his mitre on his head and carrying a crozier. He leaves toys and sweets for the children. In some parts of France he also leaves a bunch of birch rods tied round with ribbon to remind the children to be good. Most people in Germany reserve Christmas time for gift-giving. They celebrate St. Nicholas Eve as a harbinger of Christmas by having the good saint come on this day to warn the children to be good. In Belgium and Holland, the children put hay and carrots out for the white steed of St. Nicholas, and then on St. Nicholas morn hasten to see what the good saint has left for them. In Holland they place their shoes on the hearth, for in that country St. Nicholas comes down the chimney to leave his gifts.

In Belgium, St. Nicholas carries a big book so he can write down the names of the good children who will be remembered with gifts. In Holland, he is often accompanied by a servant called Black Pete. Boys and girls are told to be good lest Black Pete carry them off in his bag.

In Switzerland there are parades held in many places on St. Nicholas Day. This is a day for fetes and fairs, too, with all kinds of gifts and toys for children displayed in street booths.

In the lands across the seas there are other characters similar to St. Nicholas or Santa Claus, known by other names. In Austria and the northern part of Germany there is *Knecht Ruprecht*. He is an old man with a beard, dressed all in fur. Then there is *Pelsnichol* (Fur Nicholas) who carries a bag of coal with him to give to bad children.

In Sweden, a small elf-man called *Yultomte* takes the place of St. Nicholas. He works in secret, remaining hidden under the floor boards. But the work of Christmas would never get done without him, the children say. They place a dish of rice pudding on the floor for him before they go to bed on Yule Eve. In Norway and Denmark, little Christmas men who look like gnomes with their red, pointed caps are called *Jule-nissen*. They, too, are responsible for guarding Christmas secrets and seeing that all the chores in the house are completed in time for Yule.

Another elflike man connected with Christmas is *Bozhitch,* the little Christmas god of the Serbians. He is shown dressed in a white tunic. Many of the Christmas songs or *colleda* tell about Bozhitch, and in the Serbian language his name means Christmas. In Bulgaria, Grandfather *Koleda* is the bringer of gifts to the boys and girls. Mexican children, too, are familiar with a kindly old god at Christmas time. His name is *Quetzalcoatl,* and the Indians say he is responsible for the beauty of their warm, springlike Christmas season.

England and Australia call their Santa Claus Father Christmas. In France and in some South American countries, he is known as

JOSEPH AND THE ANGEL

Joseph, a carpenter, was engaged to be married to Mary.

An angel of the Lord came to Mary and told her she had been chosen to be the mother of Jesus, the long-expected Messiah.

Joseph was troubled by this news and unsure about what to do.

An angel came to Joseph in a dream to calm his fears and tell him about the child Jesus who would be born to Mary.

Joseph did his part. He cared for Mary and the child Jesus.

Joseph was faithful to God, and he cared or Mary and the boy Jesus. How do we rve God in our families?

". . . an angel of the Lord appeared to him i
a dream, saying, 'Joseph, son of David, do
not fear to take Mary your wife, . . . she wil
bear a son, and you shall call his name
Jesus, . . .'"

—*Matthew 1:20-2*

Papa Noël. Though he resembles our Santa somewhat, he is more of a religious character. In some sections of Switzerland it is Father Christmas and his wife who leave gifts at the various homes in the village.

Then there is St. Lucia. St. Lucia's Day, December thirteenth, is the beginning of the Christmas season in some parts of Switzerland.

In Czechoslovakia there is *Svaty Mikulas,* Saint Nicholas, who is said to have descended straight from heaven on a golden cord to distribute gifts to the children.

The Greeks have St. Basil. The carolers sing hymns about him on New Year's Eve and receive gifts of money from the listeners.

There are children in Finland who receive their Christmas gifts from a traditional national hero by the name of *Wainamoinen.* Other boys and girls of this country know *Ukko* as the bringer of gifts. Some people think this old bearded man with his red coat and white cap, from this far northern snowy country, is probably the model of our own Santa Claus.

In most of these characters from the nations around the world we can see some similarity to our Santa Claus. But to American children Santa seems to be distinctly an American character; they like him just as he is and want no other to take his place.

But how about the Wise Men and their influence on gift-giving at Christmas? We know the story of how the Wise Men of the East took their gifts to the newborn Christ Child. This was several days after the birth, and the anniversary of that day is Epiphany. There are several names for the Eve of Epiphany. In England it is called Twelfth Night. In other places it is known as the Day of the Three Kings, Little Christmas and Old Christmas. Actually it is Old Christmas, for by the Julian or Old Style calendar which some churches still follow for their feast days, Christmas came on this day.

By our present calendar Epiphany comes January sixth. It is on that day that gifts are exchanged in many countries of the Roman Catholic faith instead of on Christmas Day. In many places, including Italy, Spain, and Central and South American countries, children put their shoes outside the door or on the balcony so that the Magi, the Wise Men, may find them easily and leave their gifts. In Puerto Rico, the children put boxes on top of the house to receive gifts from the Magi, who are said to leap across the rooftops.

In Belgium the children celebrate Epiphany by singing carols in groups on the streets, and coins are given the singers.

In Yugoslavia it is said that on the day of Epiphany the heavens open so that the Christ Child may better hear what gifts are desired.

Elsewhere in this book the story of La Befana is told. La Befana is a corruption of the word La Epiphania. She is the woman or good fairy who brings gifts to Italian children. In recent years she has appeared as a young woman dressed in white, but originally La Befana was always pictured as an old woman with a bell in one hand and a bag in the other. She announced her arrival at each house by ringing her bell. For good children her pack contained sweets and gifts, but bad children were told that La Befana had a supply of ashes in that bag, too. If they didn't want ashes filling their shoes on the morning of Epiphany they had better please old Befana! In some pictures she was shown carrying a broom and a basket.

In the city of Rome each year a wonderful Befana Fair is held, a place of dreams come true for little children! Booths are set up in the Piazza Navona, and such booths they are, filled with every kind of doll and game and spinning top and mechanical toy that children dream of! Some of the booths sell candy and nuts and fruits and cakes. Girls and boys go about looking at everything and tooting their Befana whistles and trying to add to the sounds that seem to be coming from every side at once. There is a saying that the noisier the Befana Fair the better time everyone has!

In Italy, the gifts are sometimes found on Epiphany Eve in a large crock called the Urn of Fate. To add to the fun, some members of the family draw a blank before receiving their gift. The Urn of Fate, hundreds of years ago, was used by the ancient Romans to tell fortunes; Italian children think its present use is far more exciting.

Mexican children put their shoes outside the door on Epiphany Eve to receive their gifts. But there is still another "gift" that all Mexican children look forward to. It comes in a *pinata* in a shower of good things to eat on Christmas Eve, right after the last *Posada* has been celebrated. When this religious enactment of the Nativity is over, everyone feels gay and ready for fun. And fun it is! All the family and guests and servants gather together in the patio where the *pinata* has been swung up on ropes to hang over the center of the court. The *pinata* is really a jar (*olla*) which has been cleverly disguised. These *pinatas* can be bought in almost any size or shape the family desires. They are made to look like birds or animals, or they may be a jolly fat man with a round belly, or a wonderful ship, a shoe, a house, or just a very fancy pottery bowl with streamers and flounces of tissue paper gaily adorning it. Anyway, the inside is more important than the outside, for the *pinata* is stuffed to the top with delicious candies or nuts or bon-bons, or all three, together with tiny toys and whistles and knickknacks. When it is time to break the *pinata*, each child is blindfolded, given a stick, turned about three times, and set on his merry way to try to find the *pinata* and strike it with the stick. Needless to say the fun of the game goes on for some time before some child actually hits the *pinata* with the stick, hard enough to break it and send the contents scattering over the ground! The mad scramble that follows brings the game to a grand climax.

In Syria, the land where Jesus was born, it is said that the Littlest Camel brings the gifts, so the boys and girls always remember to set out water and grain for him.

In many places, the boys and girls look to the little Christ Child himself to bring their gifts on Christmas Eve. In most places, it is true, the Holy Child remains out of sight but there is always plenty of proof that He has made His annual visit. He is credited sometimes with the entire preparations for His anniversary, from trimming the tree to filling the stockings or shoes, as the custom demands.

In Germany and parts of Switzerland, the children call him *Christkindel,* which sounds very much like our Kriss Kringle. In Swiss villages where he is *Christkindli,* he often appears as an angel dressed in white with golden wings and crown. The children watch for the angel as he (or she) drives over snow-covered roads in a sleigh filled with gifts and Christmas trees. When Christkindli arrives in the homes of Holland and Germany he announces his arrival with the shout of *"Yulklapp!"* which means "Gifts!" This word came from the old custom of clapping or striking against the door and then tossing the gift into the house much as St. Nicholas did during his days upon earth. Now a white sheet is spread upon the floor just within the entrance to catch the sweets and fruit and toys that *Christkindli* tosses there with his cry of *"Yulklapp!"*

Children of France, who fill their shoes with hay on Epiphany Eve for the camels of the Magi, place their shoes beside the bed on Christmas Eve for the *Petit Jesu* (little Jesus) to fill with gifts.

Spanish children of the Philippines call their gift-bearer *Santo Nino.* There, the children march in a Christmas procession after church services are over. They carry flowers and strew them along the way in honor of the little Christ Child who has been so good to them.

The Mexicans give small plays in honor of the Christ Child during the two weeks from Christmas to Epiphany. These were originally brought to Mexico from Spain by Spanish monks years ago. The plays, called *pastores,* always point a moral and are given purely for their spiritual effect rather than for entertainment.

Although Italian children know that Befana brings their gifts on Epiphany Eve, they know, too, that it is *Il Santissimo Bambino* who comes on the eve of His birthday. They feel very friendly toward the Holy Child. He is familiar to them through the sacred art of their churches, and they pay homage to Him on the anniversary of His birth.

In our question as to how the custom of gift-giving at Christmas began, we promised to explore all the various clues. We have seen how, in centuries gone by, it was customary for monarchs and other rulers to extract gifts from their subjects on certain holidays. We have followed the legends of St. Nicholas and his retinue of gift-bearers. On the serious side we have explored the stories of the Wise Men and the Epiphany, and the saints who in one way or another became connected with Christmas. Finally, in our quest, we discovered that the Christ Child Himself is in some places credited with bringing Christmas gifts.

And the answer? We have seen that there isn't just one answer. The answer is a mixture and a melding of all the influences we have explored. Is it Santa Claus who brings the gifts? The answer is yes. Is it the Wise Men? The answer is yes. Is it the Christ Child? Again the answer is yes. For all these beings are an expression of love—love for the little Christ Child whose birthday we celebrate, love for those with whom we exchange gifts.

In the year 1897 a little girl named Virginia wrote a letter to the editor of the *New York Sun* asking, "Is there a Santa Claus?" In his now famous reply to her question the editor answered:

"The most real things in the world are those that neither children nor men can see. Did you ever see fairies dancing on the lawn? Of course not, but that's no proof that they are not there. Nobody can conceive or imagine all the wonders there are unseen and unseeable in the world. . . . Only faith, fancy, poetry, love, romance, can push aside that curtain and view and picture the supernatural beauty and glory beyond. . . .

"No Santa Claus? Thank God he lives, and he lives forever. A thousand years from now, Virginia, nay, ten thousand years from now, he will continue to make glad the heart of childhood."

And so we know that no matter who we believe is the giver of gifts at Christmas time—Santa Claus, La Befana, the Bambino—that person is very real to us as the Spirit of Christmas in our hearts.

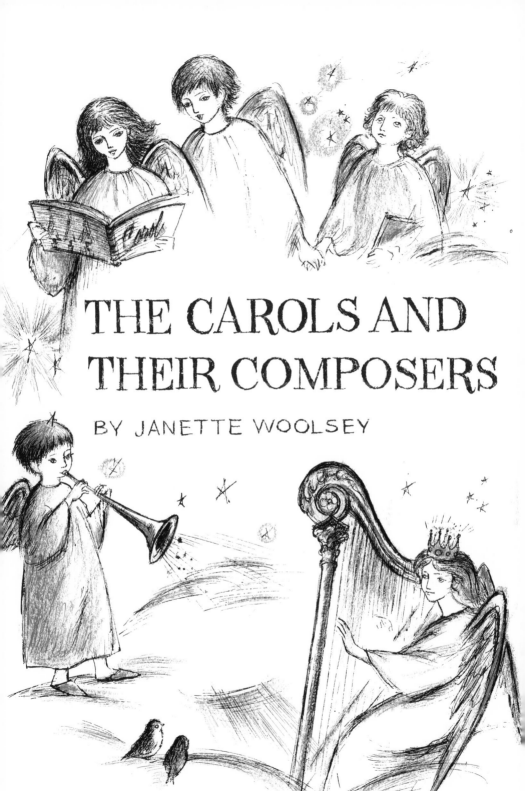

THE CAROLS AND
THEIR COMPOSERS

BY JANETTE WOOLSEY

The Carols and Their Composers

"There's a song in the air." This first line of a lovely carol written by Josiah G. Holland, an American poet, is a most fitting description of the Christmas season. For everywhere that Christ's birth is honored, it is celebrated in song.

To celebrate a particular event in song, however, was not original with Christians. As far back as the Greeks and Romans hymns were sung in honor of the gods and goddesses. And in their temples, the Hebrews sang to the glory of God. Indeed, throughout the ages singing has always been a part of almost every festival. So it was very natural that the Nativity of Christ should be observed the same way. Historians have told us that the custom of singing Christmas carols goes back as early as the year 129.

Although most of the carols that are popular today are of comparatively recent origin, some that we sing are so old that no one is just sure when they were written or by whom. Most of the early carols were written in Latin and were used in connection with the Nativity plays. Some people like to think that St. Francis of Assisi was really the father of the Christmas carol as we know it today as among his followers he promoted the idea of singing at the Christmas season.

Every Christian country has its own caroling traditions. Italy has always enjoyed holiday singing. The shepherds in the mountains there used to come down from their homes late in November to sing carols in the city streets, and often afterwards they'd be invited to sing in private homes. When they returned to the hills they felt well rewarded with all the gifts that had been given them for their efforts.

In Spain, carol singing at home around the Christmas manger scene is a time-honored custom. In Portugal, bands of singers journey from house to house. Often they are invited in and treated to good things to eat.

In the Scandinavian countries there are always special carol services for children in the churches. In Poland, Hungary and Czechoslovakia, carolers march around carrying a star. In France people put lighted candles in their windows so that carolers will stop and sing for them. And in Germany, families enjoy singing together around their own lighted Christmas trees.

In England, back in medieval days, minstrels traveled from castle to castle at the Christmas season, entertaining the lord of the castle and his guests with Christmas songs. Sometimes the songs were of a reverent nature but often they were in celebration of bringing in the Yule log or passing the wassail bowl. In later years these professional singers were known as waits and groups of them traveled together from farm to farm and from castle to manor house. But eventually this custom fell into bad repute, as the singers carried money boxes for Christmas contributions and beggars took advantage of the custom.

Today, however, in England there are still carolers who go about singing at homes in their neighborhood and take great pride in the excellence of their performance.

In America in the days of the Pilgrims, carol singing was frowned upon in New England. Indeed, those stern Pilgrim Fathers forbade any jollity at all in the celebration of Christmas. But in New Orleans, New Amsterdam, Virginia and Pennsylvania, the settlers enjoyed singing carols to their hearts' content.

Nowadays caroling has become a recognized part of the Christmas season in the United States. Many towns and cities have community Christmas trees, and carol singing around them is an accepted tradition. Groups of carolers visit hospitals and shut-ins. In some department stores busy shoppers take time out at certain hours in the day to join together in singing the familiar songs. In York, Pennsylvania, on Christmas Eve, carols are played on a factory whistle! Sometimes caroling groups are professional singers but more often they are just persons who enjoy singing the beloved songs.

Although we know the carols and have heard them often, we are not so familiar with the persons who wrote them or the circumstances that caused them to be written. So let us get acquainted with the poets who helped to celebrate the tidings of "Peace on earth, good will to men" throughout the world.

O COME, ALL YE FAITHFUL

One of the lovely Christmas carols used by churches all over the Christian world is "O Come, All Ye Faithful." And, as in the case of many hymns which have come down to us from long ago, there is doubt as to its authorship. The only thing that seems certain is that it was written a long, long time ago. But, even so, students of Christmas carols disagree just how long ago that was.

Many persons, including Hendrik W. Van Loon, who wrote a book on Christmas carols, think it was written by St. Bonaventure in the thirteenth century. Van Loon believed it was originally written in Latin and was sung around the Christmas crèche. St. Bonaventure, a French monk born in the year 1221, was a devoted follower of St. Francis of Assisi and was considered his greatest successor. Although St. Bonaventure was the author of many works this carol is not to be found in any of them.

O COME, ALL YE FAITHFUL

BY JOHN FRANCIS WADE (?)

O come, all ye faithful,
Joyful and triumphant,
(Adeste fideles, laeti triumphantes)
O come ye, O come ye to Bethlehem!
(Venite, venite in Bethlehem)
Come and behold Him,
Born the King of Angels!
(Natum videte, Regem angelorum)
   O come, let us adore Him,
   O come, let us adore Him,
   (Venite, adoremus, venite, adoremus)
   O come, let us adore Him,
   Christ the Lord!
   (Venite, adoremus Dominum)

Sing choirs of Angels
Sing in exaltation
(Cantet nunc Io chorus angelorum)
Sing all ye citizens of heav'n above;
(Cantet nunc aula coelestium)
Glory to God—
In the highest glory!
(Gloria, gloria in excelsis Deo)
   O come, let us adore Him,
   O come, let us adore Him,
   (Venite, adoremus, venite, adoremus)
   O come, let us adore Him,
   Christ the Lord!
   (Venite, adoremus Dominum)

Yea, Lord, we greet Thee,
Born this happy morning,
(Ergo qui natus die hodierna)
Jesus, to Thee
Be all glory giv'n;
(Jesu, tibi sit gloria)
Word of the Father,
Now in flesh appearing;
(Patris aeterni verbum caro factum)
   O come, let us adore Him,
   O come, let us adore Him,
   (Venite, adoremus, venite, adoremus)
   O come, let us adore Him,
   Christ, the Lord!
   (Venite, adoremus Dominum)

Sometimes "O Come, All Ye Faithful" is known as the "Portuguese Hymn." And, again, different reasons have been given for this. Some have claimed it was because the music was composed by Marcus Portugalo, who was the conductor of a London choir. There were others who have said it was called the "Portuguese Hymn" because it was sung so often by the choir in the Portuguese Chapel in London. And still others have believed that it got its name because it originated in Portugal. Recent discoveries have led to the belief that this beautiful carol was probably written by John Francis Wade.

John Francis Wade, born in 1712, was an Englishman but made his home in Douai, France. It was his business to copy music for Catholic institutions and in 1751 he made a copy of this song for the Roman Catholic College in Lisbon, Portugal. It probably became known as the "Portuguese Hymn" because it was used so frequently in the Lisbon College.

Although nothing positive has been proved about the composer, it does seem certain that the carol was written originally for the Catholic Church. For many years it was known as the "Midnight Mass" and the members of religious orders chanted it as they walked to the church to prepare for the sermon on Christmas morning. Because it was first sung in Latin it is also familiarly known as "Adeste Fideles" which, translated, means "Come hither, ye faithful."

"Adeste Fideles" is a carol sung now in churches of all faiths. For many people its stirring melody and its joyful message has made it their favorite Christmas song.

JOY TO THE WORLD

One of the customs of nineteenth century schools, usually on Friday afternoons, was the speaking of pieces. And one poem which was most often recited went in part like this:

> *How doth the little busy bee*
> *Improve each shining hour,*
> *And gather honey all the day*
> *From every opening flow'r!*
>
> *In works of labor or of skill*
> *I would be busy too;*
> *For Satan finds some mischief still*
> *For idle hands to do.*

Poems that had a moral were most popular with teachers of that period! Boys and girls learned, too, who wrote the poems they recited and could have said quickly that the lines quoted above came from the pen of Isaac Watts.

Isaac Watts was born in England in 1674. His childhood must have been none too pleasant. His father was often in trouble for his nonconformist ideas. It has been told that when Isaac was still a babe in his mother's arms she used to carry him to St. Michael's prison in Southhampton so his father could see him from the barred windows.

When Isaac was two years old his father, on being released from prison for the third time, was ordered to leave town. For two years the family lived in London more or less in hiding. Then his father, emerging once more into public life, became a clothier and in time was quite well-to-do.

Isaac was a very precocious child and his father, taking advantage of his ability to learn easily, began to give him instruction in Latin at the age of four. By the time he was eight years old he was taking lessons in Greek. When he was eleven he could speak French and by the time he was fourteen he was studying Hebrew! But he had one habit that annoyed his family very much. He liked to talk in meter and much of his conversation was in rhyme. And this manner of speaking was not considered respectful to his elders.

As Isaac grew into young manhood he became very independent in his thinking. His religious beliefs were those of a nonconformist like his father. Although his father could well afford to send him to Oxford he refused to go, since at Oxford he would have been obliged to accept the Anglican Church and he preferred the Calvinist teachings. At the age of twenty-six he became pastor of a church of that faith. As a pastor he was beloved by his parishioners. So much so, in fact, that he was retained at one church all his life.

Isaac Watts was not a handsome man. Indeed, he was considered quite ugly. He was short of stature, being only about five feet tall. His head was unusually large and it seemed even more so because he wore a huge wig! He had a hooked nose, small piercing eyes and a pock-scarred face caused by smallpox suffered at the age of nine. He never married, although it is told that he carried on a romantic courtship by correspondence with a young lady who had fallen in love with his poetry. After seeing him she refused to marry him, but they always remained good friends.

One of his wealthy parishioners was Sir Thomas Abney who at one time was Lord Mayor of London. He had a country estate and invited Watts to be a weekend guest. Watts accepted the invitation but he didn't stay just a weekend. Instead, he stayed for thirty-six years, remaining with the Abney family until his death. This must certainly be the longest visit on record!

During his lifetime Isaac Watts wrote many books on various

subjects, including grammar, pedagogy, ethics, psychology, sermons and poetry. Many of his poems were set to music and are still sung in churches today. Two of his well known hymns are "When I Survey the Wondrous Cross" and "O God Our Help in Ages Past." The Ninety-eighth Psalm was a great inspiration to Isaac Watts. The words stirred him deeply.

> *. . . Make a joyful noise unto the Lord, all the earth:*
> *make a loud noise, and rejoice, and sing praise.*
> *Sing unto the Lord with the harp;*
> *with the harp, and the voice of a psalm.*
> *With trumpets, and sound of cornet,*
> *make a joyful noise before the Lord, the King.*
> *Let the sea roar, and the fulness thereof;*
> *the world, and they that dwell therein.*
> *Let the floods clap their hands:*
> *let the hills be joyful together*
> *Before the Lord; for he cometh to judge the earth:*
> *with righteousness shall he judge the world,*
> *and the people with equity.*

This psalm of great rejoicing inspired Isaac Watts to write a hymn of joy and gladness. And each Christmas people all over the world let their voices ring out loud and clear in his carol that expresses such complete joy in the coming of the Lord.

JOY TO THE WORLD

BY ISAAC WATTS (1674–1748)

Joy to the world! the Lord is come:
  Let earth receive her King:
Let every heart prepare Him room,
  And heaven and nature sing,
  And heaven and nature sing,
And heaven, and heaven and nature sing.

Joy to the world! the Saviour reigns:
  Let men their songs employ:
While fields and floods, rocks, hills, and plains
  Repeat the sounding joy,
  Repeat the sounding joy,
Repeat, repeat the sounding joy.

No more let sins and sorrows grow,
  Nor thorns infest the ground;
He comes to make His blessings flow
  Far as the curse is found,
  Far as the curse is found,
Far as, far as the curse is found.

He rules the world with truth and grace,
  And makes the nations prove
The glories of His righteousness,
  And wonders of His love,
  And wonders of His love,
And wonders, and wonders of His love.

HARK! THE HERALD ANGELS SING

On December 18, 1707, there was rejoicing in the home of the Reverend Samuel Wesley and his wife, Susanna. For on this day their son Charles was born.

Life was not easy for the Wesley family. Charles was the eighteenth child and there was to be a nineteenth too, a little girl, Kezia. The town of Epworth in the County of Lincolnshire, England, was not a religious community and many of its residents treated their minister cruelly. Sometimes his crops were burned, sometimes his cattle were stoned, and once his house caught on fire under most mysterious circumstances.

But even with all the hardships the family had to undergo their home life was a happy one. To be sure, with so many children Mrs. Wesley had to be very strict. The children were taught to be tidy or suffer the penalty. But there were always interesting things going on too. Susanna Wesley became very much involved with a missionary movement and offered her home for meetings. Charles and his older brother John were permitted to attend and they listened eagerly to all they heard about converting nonbelievers to Christianity.

Charles's early education began at home but when he was old enough he was sent to the Westminster School for further study. About this time, when he was fourteen years old, a wealthy Irishman became interested in the boy and offered to adopt him and make him his heir. But Charles couldn't bear the thought of breaking his close family relationships and he refused.

After completing his education at Westminster School Charles went to Oxford, where his brother John was already a student.

John, a deeply religious young man, had got together a group of like-minded students and they met, as they said, to improve their minds by study and discussion. Charles soon became a member of this group too. The other students at Oxford ridiculed it and called it "The Holy Club." Later, because Charles and his friends insisted on certain "methods" of worship they became known as the "Methodists."

In 1732, under the leadership of General James Oglethorpe, Georgia had become an independent colony. The colony was founded originally to provide new homes and to give new opportunity for making a living to people of unfortunate circumstances in England. But things didn't turn out as successfully as the founder had anticipated. The people were extravagant, they didn't get along well with one another, and many scandals arose. So General Oglethorpe and the other trustees looked around to see whom they might send over to help bring about a change in the people's way of living. And they decided upon the two Wesley brothers, John and Charles. John, who had been ordained, was to be minister and Charles was to be General Oglethorpe's secretary.

In 1735 the Wesleys sailed for America. On the way over on shipboard they kept to their rigorous way of living. Most of each day was spent in prayer and meditation and in the evenings they joined with a group of Moravian settlers in a song-fest. It is said that from his association with this group Charles received much inspiration for some of the later hymns he wrote.

The American venture, however, proved too strenuous for Charles. He was forced to return to England at the end of a year because of ill health. Some time later John returned also, and once more the Wesley brothers began preaching from place to place and establishing "Methodist" societies all over England.

Charles soon became known not only for his preaching but also for the beautiful hymns he composed. He taught these to people wherever he preached. Later, after his marriage to the beautiful and deeply religious Sarah Gwynne, he gave up traveling but still continued to write hymns. It is said that he composed over six thousand spiritual songs. Two of the best known are "Jesus, Lover of My Soul" and "Love Divine, All Love Excelling."

One of the best-loved Christmas carols is a song written by Charles Wesley. It is "Hark! the Herald Angels Sing," written in 1739. The tune we use now was not the one to which it was first sung. In 1855, after Charles Wesley had been dead for sixty-seven years, William H. Cummings set it to a tune which Felix Mendelssohn had composed earlier. Although Mendelssohn had composed the music in commemoration of the anniversary of the invention of printing, and had not intended it to be used in a religious setting, this melody of Mendelssohn's and the words of Charles Wesley are most suitably adapted to one another.

HARK! THE HERALD ANGELS SING

BY CHARLES WESLEY, 1707–1788

Hark! the herald angels sing,
"Glory to the newborn King;
Peace on earth, and mercy mild,
God and sinners reconciled!"
Joyful, all ye nations, rise,
Join the triumph of the skies;
With the angelic host proclaim,
"Christ is born in Bethlehem!"
Hark! the herald angels sing,
"Glory to the newborn King!"

Christ, by highest heav'n adored:
Christ, the Everlasting Lord!
Late in time behold Him come,
Offspring of the Virgin's womb;
Veiled in flesh the Godhead see;
Hail the incarnate Deity,
Pleased as man with men to dwell,
Jesus, our Emmanuel.
                    Refrain

Hail, the heaven-born Prince of Peace!
Hail, the Sun of Righteousness!
Light and life to all He brings,
Risen with healing in His wings.
Mild He lays His glory by,
Born that man no more may die,
Born to raise the sons of earth,
Born to give them second birth.
                    Refrain

IT CAME UPON
THE MIDNIGHT CLEAR

On a cold wintry day in the year 1850, a minister, Edmund Sears, sat at his study window in Wayland, Massachusetts, looking out at the snow-covered landscape. Although the scene before him was peaceful there were signs that it might not be so for long. Just four years ago the country had been involved in a war with Mexico. This had finally ended in a peace treaty ceding the United States its claims to Texas, California, Arizona, New Mexico, Nevada, Utah and part of Colorado.

But already there was trouble brewing in the United States itself. The issue was slavery and whether or not it should be allowed in the new territories. Senator Henry Clay had been hard at work trying to get laws passed that would please both sides—those who wanted slavery and those who didn't. Even the compromises that Clay was suggesting were not the final solution. One day the matter would be resolved at the expense of bloodshed, with brother fighting against brother. The Civil War was not far off from this peaceful day in 1850.

The New England of the day when Edmund Sears sat at his study window was far different from the New England of today. There were few bustling, industrial cities at that time. It was only in recent years that the first railroad had been completed in Massachusetts. The horse and buggy was still the accepted method of transportation and most people stayed close to their villages and towns.

There were numerous small villages dotted over the countryside. These usually, no matter how small, had four churches clustered about the quiet village green: a Baptist, a Congregational, a Unitarian and an Episcopal. Of course there was a general store, which carried everything from crackers to clothing.

The coastal towns' main interest was the building and sailing of clipper ships and whalers. Towns were beginning to grow up around factories that manufactured farm tools and plows that had cast iron shares instead of wooden ones.

It was a day when people liked to boast of their age, and claims of being over a hundred were not uncommon. And it was a day of huge meals. There are accounts of travelers who were served eggs, fried pork, beefsteak, buckwheat cakes, apple tarts, pickles, cheese, cider and tea for breakfast!

It was a day when writers lived whose names would go down in literary history: Henry Wadsworth Longfellow, Ralph Waldo Emerson, John Greenleaf Whittier, Washington Irving, Herman Melville, Harriet Beecher Stowe and Oliver Wendell Holmes.

And it was a day when Christmas was not celebrated as a holiday in families brought up in the Puritan tradition.

As Edmund Sears sat there that wintry day perhaps he recalled his own boyhood. He was born at Sandisfield, Massachusetts, on April 6, 1810. His father was a farmer and, although a respected man in his community, not a wealthy one. Edmund was brought up knowing what it meant to work hard.

Even as a young boy he was interested in learning and he had a strong determination to go to college. But this seemed an almost unattainable desire. At that time boys started to school at an early age and some were ready to enter college when they were fourteen. But Edmund Sears had to wait and it was not until he was twenty-one that he was able to enter Union College. By studying diligently he completed his college course in three years. He decided to enter the ministry and enrolled at Harvard Divinity School. After graduation he preached for a time at a mission in Toledo, Ohio, and then in 1839 was ordained a minister in the Unitarian Church. Although he received many calls to large and wealthy churches he preferred country parishes. For one thing his health was never too robust, but also he wanted more time for writing. From the time he was young he loved to write and was the author of many religious books, besides being the editor of a monthly magazine. This year of 1850 would be memorable for Edmund Sears. For it was the year he married Ellen Bacon of Barnstable.

As he looked out the window at the quietly falling snow he must have felt very keenly the desire for peace which is in the hearts of men all over the world.

"Peace on earth, good will toward men," was the song the angels sang that night of Christ's birth in Bethlehem. As he remembered the promise that was made it must have seemed to him that no matter how difficult life is at times and no matter what troubles beset the world there still is the hope of peace for mankind. It is this hope that Edmund Sears expressed so beautifully in the carol he wrote that wintry day.

IT CAME UPON THE MIDNIGHT CLEAR

BY EDMUND H. SEARS

It came upon the midnight clear,
  That glorious song of old,
From angels bending near the earth,
  To touch their harps of gold:
"Peace on the earth, good will to men,
  From heaven's all-gracious King:"
The world in solemn stillness lay,
  To hear the angels sing.

Still through the cloven skies they come,
  With peaceful wings unfurled,
And still their heavenly music floats
  O'er all the weary world:
Above its sad and lowly plains
  They bend on hovering wing,
And ever o'er its Babel sounds
  The blessed angels sing.

O ye, beneath life's crushing load,
  Whose forms are bending low,
Who toil along the climbing way
  With painful steps and slow,
Look now! for glad and golden hours
  Come swiftly on the wing:
O rest beside the weary road,
  And hear the angels sing.

For lo! the days are hastening on,
  By prophet bards foretold,
When with the ever-circling years
  Comes round the age of gold;
When peace shall over all the earth
  Its ancient splendors fling,
And the whole world give back the song
  Which now the angels sing.

Early in December of 1865 a young man arrived in Damascus to visit the Holy Land and to become familiar with those places where Jesus had lived and had taught his followers. This young man was Phillips Brooks, Episcopal rector of the Church of the Holy Trinity in Philadelphia, Pennsylvania.

Although only thirty years old, Phillips Brooks was already recognized as a powerful church leader. He was born in Boston December 13, 1835. His family was a religious one and prayers in the morning and evening were a part of the daily routine. Phillips was educated at the Latin School, a private institution, and at Harvard. He proved himself an excellent student and graduated from college at the age of nineteen.

At first Phillips thought that he wanted to teach and accepted an offer in the school he had formerly attended, the Latin School. But it was his misfortune to have assigned to him a class of particularly mischievous boys. These boys were from fifteen to seventeen years of age and as he was but twenty they soon proved too much for him to handle. So, being unhappy in his teaching, he resigned his position. It was at this time that his thoughts turned toward the ministry. Phillips Brooks had made a wise choice and he became one of the most outstanding churchmen of his time.

The trip he took to Europe and the Holy Land came just after the end of the Civil War. For some time he had desired to go but conditions in this country had of course made even the thought of it impossible. Now he could enjoy every minute of it. He left home in August and the first three months were spent visiting spots of interest in Europe. It was early in December when he at last came to that part of the trip to which he had looked forward for so long—the journey to Palestine.

All during that visit as he traveled up and down the country he found himself reliving both Old and New Testament history. And he felt that the presence of Christ filled the landscape in Palestine.

Palestine itself seemed hardly changed from Biblical days. There were the mountains, brown and scorched by the hot sun. How different they seemed from the green, tree-covered ones to which he was accustomed! And there were the camels and donkeys, sometimes used to draw ploughs over the fields and sometimes laden with the household goods of families on a journey. And there were the cities that he must have known by heart. Jerusalem, with its narrow streets so steep that steps had to be built to climb them; the shops on either side filled with merchants crying their wares—all these things made deep impressions on him. But as he journeyed through the countryside on horseback, he kept thinking how Christ must have felt. It seemed to him as he visited the Sea of Galilee, the hill where Christ fed the multitude, and Nazareth, that the way was marked with the footprints of the Master.

On Christmas Eve he came to Bethlehem. Surely this was the one night in the whole year when he wanted to be in the city of Christ's birth. As he journeyed to Bethlehem the story of that holy night became more and more vivid to him. Riding through the countryside as he approached the city he could almost feel the presence of the shepherds who had been tending their flocks when the Angel of the Lord appeared before them. Bethlehem itself, quiet on this holy night, the anniversary of the Saviour's birth, seemed to him to be the symbol of all men's fears and hopes for generations past and those to come.

The memory of this night never left him and later back in Philadelphia he wrote the carol that was soon to become so popular. It was sung first by the children of his Sunday school in 1868. As the words of "O Little Town of Bethlehem" rang out, those hearing it knew that this was a song that would be sung and loved by people everywhere.

O LITTLE TOWN OF BETHLEHEM

BY PHILLIPS BROOKS (1835–1893)

O little town of Bethlehem,
  How still we see thee lie;
Above thy deep and dreamless sleep
  The silent stars go by.
Yet in thy dark streets shineth
  The everlasting Light;
The hopes and fears of all the years
  Are met in thee tonight.

For Christ is born of Mary;
  And gathered all above,
While mortals sleep, the angels keep
  Their watch of wondering love.
O morning stars, together
  Proclaim the holy birth;
And praises sing to God the King,
  And peace to men on earth!

How silently, how silently
  The wondrous gift is given!
So God imparts to human hearts
  The blessings of his heaven.
No ear may hear his coming,
  But in this world of sin,
Where meek souls will receive Him, still
  The dear Christ enters in.

O holy child of Bethlehem!
  Descend to us, we pray;
Cast out our sin, and enter in,
  Be born in us today.
We hear the Christmas angels
  The great glad tidings tell;
O come to us, abide with us,
  Our Lord Emmanuel!

[139]

If you should ask a group of small children at Christmas time what song they would like to sing, the chances are that the choice would be "Away in a Manger." And indeed, this beautiful hymn often has been called "The Children's Carol." The simplicity of the words, the pictures they bring to mind, the adaptability of the music to children's voices—all these things have contributed to its popularity.

It seems a little strange, therefore, that there has arisen such a great controversy over its authorship. But an argument over who wrote this favorite of the children has been going on for a number of years. For a long time Martin Luther was given credit for it and if you look in any number of hymn books you may find it listed as "Luther's Cradle Hymn."

Martin Luther was born in 1483 in the German mountain town of Eisleben. His father and mother were very poor and had to struggle hard to make a living for their growing family. They believed that their eldest son, Martin, had a good mind and would one day do them honor. So they determined to give him every opportunity to remain in school. And they were justified in this belief, for the name Martin Luther is an important one in history.

Brought up a Catholic, he later left the church because he came to disagree with some of its teachings and practices. At the risk of his life he began to preach the reforms that he thought should be made in the church. And those persons who followed him became known in time as "Lutherans."

From the time he was very young, Martin Luther had a very

fine singing voice and as a child was a member of the church choir. All through his life he loved to sing and to compose hymns. Many of these are still sung in Protestant churches all over the world.

In the latter part of the nineteenth century a book of songs entitled "Dainty Songs for Little Lads and Lasses," by James R. Murray, was published. Included in this collection was a song called "Luther's Cradle Hymn." Later this song became known as "Away in a Manger." Under its title in Murray's book was the explanation that Martin Luther had composed this hymn for his children and that German mothers still sang it to their little ones. This explanation of its authorship was accepted and for years "Away in a Manger" was attributed to the founder of the Lutheran church.

Recently this has been questioned, and on the basis of research work new facts have been presented. It is maintained that although there have been many biographies of Martin Luther written, none ever mentioned this song—and these biographies were based in part on the fifty-one volumes of Luther's own works. It is noted too, that the earliest versions of "Away in a Manger" have been found in English rather than in German. A Lutheran publication, *The Lutheran Companion,* which appeared in 1936, stated that "there is really no authentic information available concerning the hymn."

But after all it doesn't make too much difference. You may believe if you'd like to, as people have for years, that Martin Luther wrote it. And it may bring to your mind a picture of the great reform leader seated in the midst of his children singing this hymn to them. Or you may believe along with research scholars that no one knows exactly who wrote it or when. Children don't care about any of this.

And although the controversy may continue, when Christmas time comes the children love to sing this beloved carol which they have taken for their own.

AWAY IN A MANGER

(ANONYMOUS)

Away in a manger,
  No crib for a bed,
The little Lord Jesus
  Laid down His sweet head;
The stars in the sky
  Looked down where He lay,
The little Lord Jesus
  Asleep on the hay.

The cattle are lowing,
  The poor baby wakes,
But little Lord Jesus
  No crying He makes;
I love Thee, Lord Jesus!
  Look down from the sky,
And stay by my cradle
  Till morning is nigh.

Be near me, Lord Jesus,
  I ask Thee to stay
Close by me forever,
  And love me, I pray.
Bless all the dear children
  In thy tender care,
And take me to heaven
  To live with Thee there.

WE THREE KINGS OF ORIENT ARE

*N*ow *when Jesus was born in Bethlehem of Judaea in the days of Herod the king, behold, there came wise men from the east to Jerusalem,*

Saying, Where is he that is born King of the Jews? for we have seen his star in the east, and are come to worship him.

The story of the Wise Men as told by St. Matthew is one of the greatly loved traditional stories of the life of Jesus. Although nowhere in the Biblical story is the number of Wise Men mentioned, perhaps because of the three gifts offered it has been assumed that there were three kings. Early historians identified the travelers as Melchior, ruler of Nubia and Arabia, Caspar of Tarsus and Balthasar of Ethiopia. And the three gifts which they presented to the young Christ Child were symbolic in their meaning. Gold signified that they believed Christ to be a king, frankincense, that they believed Him divine, and the myrrh was prophetic of His death.

Very often in churches at Christmas time the story of the birth of Christ is presented in dramatic form. And whenever it is, there is one carol that is always sung. For not only is it beautiful but it is so arranged as to lend itself to dramatic presentation.

This beautiful carol, "We Three Kings of Orient Are," was written by John Henry Hopkins, Jr., in 1857. He wrote it while he was serving as Episcopal rector of Christ Church in Williamsport, Pennsylvania.

John Henry Hopkins, Jr. was born in Pittsburgh, Pennsylvania, in 1820 and he had a rather unusual boyhood. He was the son of John Henry Hopkins who later became Episcopal Bishop of

Vermont and John, Jr. was brought up according to his father's educational ideas. For one thing he never attended public school until he was ready to enter the University of Vermont. He attended a private school started by his father with theological students for teachers. No vacations and no play was the order of the day and John divided his time between study, work and church attendance. Only on Saturday afternoon did he have any time for himself. And he had to study for study's sake too, for his father did not believe that awards or even grades should be given for work accomplished.

But, besides hard work, the arts were a part of his heritage. Bishop Hopkins was an accomplished musician, artist and architect and undoubtedly instilled some of his love for music in his son. We are grateful to this young minister not only for the words, but also for the music of his popular carol.

WE THREE KINGS OF ORIENT ARE

BY JOHN HENRY HOPKINS, JR.

Kings:　　*We three kings of Orient are,*
Bearing gifts we traverse afar,
Field and fountain, moor and mountain,
Following yonder star.
Refrain

O star of wonder, star of night,
Star with royal beauty bright,
Westward leading, still proceeding,
Guide us to the perfect light.

Melchior:　*Born a babe on Bethlehem's plain*
Gold I bring to crown Him again;
King forever, ceasing never
Over us all to reign.
Refrain

Caspar:　　*Frankincense to offer have I;*
Incense owns a Deity nigh,
Prayer and praising all men raising,
Worship Him, God on high.
Refrain

Balthasar:　*Myrrh is mine; its bitter perfume*
Breathes a life of gathering gloom;
Sorrowing, sighing, bleeding, dying,
Sealed in the stone-cold tomb.
Refrain

All:　　　*Glorious now behold Him arise,*
King and God and Sacrifice;
Heaven sings "Hallelujah!"
"Hallelujah!" earth replies.
Refrain

[145]

GOOD KING WENCESLAUS

Whenever we sing Christmas carols, we are expressing our joy as we celebrate the birthday of Christ. Many of the carols tell the story of this wondrous event. But one carol that is very popular tells a different story. It is based on an old Bohemian legend about King Wenceslaus.

The story told in the carol is that King Wenceslaus, on the Feast of St. Stephen, stood looking out of his palace window. Although there was bright moonlight, it was a bitterly cold night and the frost lay heavily on the ground. Suddenly the King saw a peasant trying to find some firewood. He realized that the man in all probability needed not only fuel but food and wine as well. So he called one of his pages to him and inquired if he knew where the poor man lived. The page replied that he did but that it was a long way off. King Wenceslaus was not to be stopped in his determination to help the peasant. Ordering the page to bring food and wine and pine logs, he journeyed forth with him to help carry the provisions to the poor man's dwelling. The farther they went the harder the wind blew and the colder it seemed. Finally the page thought he could continue no longer and implored the King to allow him to return. But King Wenceslaus told him to follow along in his master's footsteps and he would be less cold. And, so the legend goes, as the servant obeyed it seemed to him that heat came from every step where the good King had trod.

Although the carol is based on a legend about King Wenceslaus, there really was such a king and he ruled Bohemia from 928 to 935 A.D.

Wenceslaus was the eldest son of King Ratislov and Queen Drahomira, rulers of Bohemia, and he was born in the year 907 near Prague. His grandmother was St. Ludmila and she requested that she be allowed to bring up the boy. Ludmila was a deeply religious woman and consequently Wenceslaus was well grounded in the teachings of the Christian Church.

When he was very young his father was killed in battle and his mother took over the government. She came under the influence of persons who were not Christians and they persuaded her that Ludmila should be put to death. But soon after this, Queen Drahomira was forced from power and Wenceslaus was proclaimed king.

During the years Wenceslaus ruled Bohemia he became renowned for his great kindness to his subjects. On Christmas day and St. Stephen's day, which is December 26th, he was most generous in his gifts to them.

Some years following his death he was proclaimed a saint by the church and was accepted as the patron saint of the Bohemian people.

The words of the carol, "Good King Wenceslaus," were written by an Englishman, John Mason Neale. He was born in London in 1818, the son of a minister. He received most of his early education at home but later won a scholarship to Trinity College at Cambridge. Always interested in religion, he studied for the ministry. During most of his life he suffered from poor health, and as the climate in England did not agree with him he spent a great deal of time on the Island of Madeira off the coast of Portugal.

From the time he was young he enjoyed composing verse and wrote almost constantly. In later years he had many religious books published. He even wrote for children, although such titles as "Stories for Children from Church History" probably would not have much appeal for young people today. But "Good King Wenceslaus" still remains a popular carol and has continued to be sung throughout the Christian world.

GOOD KING WENCESLAUS

BY JOHN MASON NEALE, 1818–1866

Good King Wenceslaus looked out
On the Feast of Stephen,
When the snow lay round about,
Deep and crisp and even;
Brightly shone the moon that night,
Though the frost was cruel,
When a poor man came in sight,
Gathering winter fuel.

"Hither, page, and stand by me,
If thou knowest it, telling;
Yonder peasant, who is he?
Where and what his dwelling?"
"Sire, he lives a good league hence,
Underneath the mountain,
Right against the forest fence,
By Saint Agnes' fountain."

"Bring me flesh, and bring me wine,
Bring me pine logs hither;
Thou and I will see him dine
When we bear them thither."
Page and monarch forth they went,
Forth they went together;
Through the rude wind's wild lament
And the bitter weather.

"Sire, the night is darker now,
And the wind blows stronger;
Fails my heart, I know not how,
I can go no longer."
"Mark my footsteps, my good page,
Tread thou in them boldly;

Thou shalt find the winter's rage
Freeze thy blood less coldly."

In his master's steps he trod,
Where the snow lay dinted;
Heat was in the very sod
Which the saint had printed.
Therefore, Christian men be sure,
Wealth or rank possessing,
Ye who now will bless the poor,
Shall yourselves find blessing.

I HEARD THE BELLS
ON CHRISTMAS DAY

"I Heard the Bells on Christmas Day," like many another Christmas carol, was not written to be sung at all. Rather it was written as a poem and not until nine years later was it set to the music that is now familiar to us.

Henry Wadsworth Longfellow, the author of this poem, was often inspired by stories he read in his morning paper or by some incident in his own personal life that moved him greatly. At such times he would sit down and, writing quickly, would soon have on paper a poem expressing his deepest emotion.

Longfellow, along with all his countrymen, was deeply concerned with the tragedy of the Civil War. And when his son Charles was severely wounded while serving with the Army of the Potomac, the tragedy became a personal one. It happened shortly after Thanksgiving Day, 1863, and the days preceding that Christmas were anxious ones for the Longfellow family. The poem, written before the New Year, expresses the grief the father felt and yet ends on a note of hope for the future of mankind. It is because this hope is universal, and because it is timeless, that this carol has as much meaning for us now as for those who lived at the time it was written.

Henry Wadsworth Longfellow was never known as a gloomy person. Rather, he was so friendly and gentle that he was known as "the Children's Poet" and was always delighted when any of his young admirers paid him a visit.

Longfellow came from a happy and understanding family. He was born in Portland, Maine, in 1807. The second of five children, he had an older brother and three younger sisters. His first years were impressionable ones and he remembered his first school, Ma'am Fellow's Infant School. Although he was sent there at the age of three, it certainly bore very little resemblance to the attractive nursery schools of today. Ma'am Fellows believed in being severe, and one of her rules was that there should be no smiling during school hours!

But later, when he was old enough to go to regular school, Henry found learning to his liking. At an early age he loved to write and often composed verses which he showed only to his mother. Once he submitted a poem, anonymously of course, to the town paper and was more than delighted when the editor printed it.

One of his early recollections was of standing on top of a hill and watching a sea battle taking place in the harbor. This was during the War of 1812, and the battle was between the British brig *The Boxer* and the American ship *The Enterprise*. Years later he recorded that event in a poem.

Henry was ready to enter college when he was fourteen but his mother thought he was too young to leave home, so he waited another year. It was just about this time that Maine became a separate state. Because of the loyalty that all its citizens felt toward this newest of states, the Longfellows chose Bowdoin College in Brunswick, Maine, for their sons rather than Harvard, which so many young New England boys attended.

Life wasn't easy in this new college but Henry studied hard and graduated third in his class. He was given the class oration to write and in it he expressed the idea that he was to carry out later in his own writings. He believed that America should have its own national literature and that American writers should not borrow old world themes. His poems, "Hiawatha," "The Courtship of Miles Standish" and "Evangeline," were one day to prove the wisdom of this belief.

Henry's father had hoped his sons would study law and become his partners. But Henry had other ideas, for he had never wavered from his ambition of having a literary life, and with his mother's encouragement to back him up he finally persuaded his father that his career lay in this direction.

Following a further year of study at Harvard and another abroad studying languages, he came home to accept a professorship at his Alma Mater, Bowdoin College. The next year he was married to Mary Potter, the daughter of one of Portland's judges. His marriage to Mary was a very happy one but of short duration, for she died the next year while they were traveling abroad. Henry had accepted a position at Harvard but it was with a heavy heart that he assumed his new duties. Looking for a room rather than for the house he had hoped to have, he found lodgings with the Widow Craigie in a house that was one day to be his own.

The next years were rewarding ones for the young professor. Not only was he successful in his teaching but he was also being acclaimed enthusiastically for his poetry. And in May of 1843 he again found happiness in his marriage to Frances Appleton, whom he had known for several years. Frances's father, knowing Henry's fondness for the house where he was living, bought Craigie House and presented it to the young couple as his wedding gift.

Although Longfellow was again to know tragedy in the death

of a little daughter and later on in that of his wife, yet he always seemed to have a quality in his writing that gave comfort and pleasure to his readers. His kindness and generosity were well known and his home became one place distinguished visitors from abroad always wanted to visit. He was known and loved all over the world and men, women and children grieved when "the Poet of Craigie House" died in 1882.

I HEARD THE BELLS ON CHRISTMAS DAY

BY HENRY WADSWORTH LONGFELLOW, 1807–1882

I heard the bells on Christmas Day
Their old, familiar carols play,
And wild and sweet
The words repeat
Of peace on earth, good will to men!

I thought how, as the day had come,
The belfries of all Christendom
Had rolled along
The unbroken song
Of peace on earth, good will to men!

And in despair I bowed my head:
"There is no peace on earth," I said,
"For hate is strong
And mocks the song
Of peace on earth, good will to men."

Then pealed the bells more loud and deep:
"God is not dead; nor doth he sleep!
The wrong shall fail
The right prevail,
With peace on earth, good will to men!"

On Christmas Eve, 1818, in the little Alpine village of Oberndorf in northern Austria it was snowing hard. The people of the little town had long before gone to bed and all was quiet and still. But there was one light still burning. It shone from the study window of the young priest, Joseph Mohr.

Joseph Mohr had not been able to go to sleep that night and he had been pacing up and down his study, pausing now and then to look out of the window at the silent, snow-covered scene before him. He was deeply worried. Christmas, a day of music and rejoicing, was almost there and as yet he had seen no way to overcome the disappointment he knew was in store for his congregation.

The truth of the matter was that the church organ was in need of repair and there was no repairman in the town of Oberndorf. And the heavy snows had made it impossible to get one from anywhere else.

He was thinking of this and at the same time was remembering a conversation he had had the preceding summer with his friend Franz Gruber, a school teacher in the town of Arnsdorf not far away. Gruber was also an accomplished musician and played the organ in the village church. One day, as was their custom, they had been sitting in the pastor's garden singing together to the accompaniment of Gruber's guitar. Suddenly Gruber had stopped in the middle of a hymn and had turned to his friend.

"Father," he had said, "do you realize that of all these Christmas songs we've been singing none expresses the real Christmas spirit?"

"You are right, my friend," the priest answered. "Perhaps one day someone will write one that will tell simply the meaning of the Holy Night."

"Why should not that someone be you?" asked the schoolmaster.

Joseph Mohr had laughed. "And will you write the music if I do?" he had asked.

"Of course," Gruber replied. "And I'm quite serious about this. I'm sure you can do it."

In the weeks that followed this conversation Joseph Mohr had tried to write that song. But somehow try as he would the words simply didn't come, and now on Christmas Eve he felt a little sad as he thought of the service the next evening with no organ and no new song to sing to his people as he had planned.

As he stood at his window now, lost in thought, he suddenly realized that someone was struggling through the deep snow toward his house. He rushed to the door and went out to help his exhausted visitor in to the warmth of his fire. It was a woman, too breathless to speak for some moments, but at last she was able to tell her story.

She had come over the mountain from the cabin of a friend of hers who that night had given birth to her first child, a son.

"And Father," the woman concluded, "her husband, who is a young woodcutter, is very anxious that you come and bless the new mother and the babe this very night."

"Of course I'll go," the priest answered.

"But the snow is getting very deep now," the woman protested. "I came as I promised him I would but I'm sure he'll understand if you wait until morning. 'Twas not snowing hard like this when I left their house."

"I don't mind the snow. And the walk will be good for me," Joseph Mohr answered. "I'm feeling too wakeful to go to bed anyway. You stay here until you're rested before you go home."

Bundling himself up in his warmest clothes and taking a stout cane to help him, the priest started out. It was several miles to the woodcutter's cabin and the heavy snow made it difficult to walk, but when he arrived and opened the door he caught his breath at the scene before him. It was one he would never forget.

[155]

There was the new mother in her bed smiling happily at her husband, who was kneeling in adoration before a crude wooden crib in which lay his newborn son. It seemed to Joseph Mohr that he was looking at a scene that had taken place in Bethlehem of Judea many ages before.

The young woodcutter felt the sudden draft of cold air and rose quickly to his feet.

"Welcome, Father," he cried. "I didn't expect you to come when I realized how hard it was snowing, but I'm grateful you're here."

Proudly he led the priest over to the cradle where the child lay and Father Mohr admired the baby and then gave him and the mother his blessing.

Although the woodcutter wanted the priest to partake of some refreshment before he left Father Mohr replied that he must be on his way. Bidding good-by to the happy parents, he set out for home—but this time the way didn't seem quite so hard. The snow was no longer falling but the branches of the pine trees bent low under their heavy white mantle. The stillness in the forest was awe-inspiring. As he plowed through the drifts the pastor kept thinking of the little family he had just left. Truly this had been a holy night.

At home, he could hardly wait to take off his coat and warm his stiff fingers. Then he sat down at his desk and began to write. It was early morning before he finished and fell exhausted upon his bed for a little rest.

But he didn't stay there long. Soon he arose, ate his breakfast and hurried out again. This time he went in the direction of Arnsdorf where his friend Franz Gruber lived. When Gruber opened his door Joseph Mohr handed him the manuscript containing the words he had written in the early morning hours. "My friend," the priest said, "here is a new Christmas song. Will you set it to music as you once promised?"

Franz Gruber's eyes shone as he read the beautiful verses. Grasping the pastor's hand he said, "I shall do my best. And we'll sing it at the service tonight. My guitar will be our accompaniment."

That evening the congregation gathered in the little church at Oberndorf to hear their priest preach his Christmas sermon. After he had finished telling them the meaning of the Star of Bethlehem, Franz Gruber came and stood with him. The altar candles cast a soft glow around them as together they sang the hymn their combined talents had produced.

As the last words, "Christ the Saviour is born," were heard, the people in the little church were filled with a reverence they had not known before. But they couldn't have realized that they were having the privilege of hearing for the first time a song that in the years to come would be the best loved of Christmas carols.

SILENT NIGHT! HOLY NIGHT!

BY JOSEPH MOHR AND FRANZ GRUBER

Silent night! Holy night!
All is calm, all is bright.
'Round yon Virgin Mother and Child!
Holy Infant, so tender and mild,
Sleep in heavenly peace,
Sleep in heavenly peace.

Silent night! Holy night!
Shepherds quake at the sight!
Glories stream from heaven afar,
Heav'nly hosts sing, "Alleluia!"
Christ, the Savior, is born!
Christ, the Savior, is born!

Silent night! Holy night!
Son of God, love's pure light!
Radiant beams from Thy holy face
With the dawn of redeeming grace,
Jesus, Lord, at Thy birth,
Jesus, Lord, at Thy birth.

CHRISTMAS
POEMS

WORDS FROM AN OLD SPANISH CAROL

TRANSLATED BY RUTH SAWYER

Shall I tell you who will come
   to Bethlehem on Christmas Morn,
who will kneel them gently down
   before the Lord, new-born?

One small fish from the river,
   with scales of red, red gold,
one wild bee from the heather,
   one grey lamb from the fold,
one ox from the high pasture,
   one black bull from the herd,
one goatling from the far hills,
   one white, white bird.

And many children—God give them grace,
bringing tall candles to light Mary's face.

Shall I tell you who will come
   to Bethlehem on Christmas Morn,
who will kneel them gently down
   before the Lord, new-born?

SIX GREEN SINGERS

BY ELEANOR FARJEON

The frost of the moon fell over my floor
And six green singers stood at my door.
"What do ye here that music make?"
"Let us come in for Christ's sweet Sake."
"Long have ye journeyed in coming here?"
"Our Pilgrimage was the length of the year."
"Where do ye make for?" I asked of them.
"Our Shrine is a Stable in Bethlehem."
"What will ye do as ye go along?"
"Sing to the world an evergreen song."
"What will ye sing for the listening earth?"
"One will sing of a brave-souled Mirth,
"One of the Holiest Mystery,
The Glory of glories shall one song be,
"One of the Memory of things,
One of the Child's imaginings,
"One of our songs is the fadeless Faith,
And all are the Life more mighty than death."
"Ere ye be gone that music make,
Give me an alms for Christ's sweet Sake."
"Six green branches we leave with you;
See they be scattered your house-place through.
"This staunch blithe Holly your board shall grace,
Mistletoe bless your chimney place,
"Laurel to crown your lighted hall,
Over your bed let the Yew-bough fall,
"Close by the cradle the Christmas Fir,
For elfin dreams in its branches stir,
"Last and loveliest, high and low,
From ceil to floor let the Ivy go."
From each glad guest I received my gift
And then the latch of my door did lift—
"Green singers, God prosper the song ye make
As ye sing to the world for Christ's sweet Sake."

HE CAME ALL SO STILL

UNKNOWN

He came all so still
Where His mother was,
As dew in April
That falleth on the grass.

He came all so still
Where His mother lay,
As dew in April
That falleth on the spray.

He came all so still
To His mother's bower,
As dew in April
That falleth on the flower.

Mother and maiden
Was never none but she!
Well might such a lady
God's mother be.

THE JOY OF GIVING

BY JOHN GREENLEAF WHITTIER

Somehow, not only for Christmas
  But all the long year through,
The joy that you give to others
  Is the joy that comes back to you;
And the more you spend in blessing
  The poor and lonely and sad,
The more of your heart's possessing
  Returns to make you glad.

TO A CHRISTMAS TREE

BY FRANCES FROST

O balsam tree, that lately held
The stars like nesting birds among
Your emerald branches, listen now
To children's voices sweet with song!

You talker with the wind, and friend
Of fox and fawn and silver mouse,
Bearing your tinsel and your gifts,
Glow softly now within this house,

Bringing your fragrance to our hearts,
Assuring us that wars will cease.
For a Child's bright birthday shine with faith,
O tree of loveliness and peace!

THE SONG OF A SHEPHERD-BOY AT BETHLEHEM

BY JOSEPHINE PRESTON PEABODY

Sleep, Thou little Child of Mary:
    Rest Thee now.
Though these hands be rough from shearing
    And the plough,
Yet they shall not ever fail Thee,
When the waiting nations hail Thee,
Bringing palms unto their King.
    Now—I sing.
Sleep, Thou little Child of Mary,
    Hope divine.
If Thou wilt but smile upon me,
    I will twine
Blossoms for Thy garlanding.
Thou'rt so little to be King,
    God's Desire!
    Not a brier
Shall be left to grieve Thy brow;
    Rest Thee now.
Sleep, Thou little Child of Mary.
    Some fair day
Wilt Thou, as Thou wert a brother,
    Come away
Over hills and over hollow?
All the lambs will up and follow,
Follow but for love of Thee.
    Lov'st Thou me?
Sleep, Thou little Child of Mary;
    Rest Thee now.
I that watch am come from sheep-stead
    And from plough.
Thou wilt have disdain of me
When Thou'rt lifted, royally,
Very high for all to see:
    Smilest Thou?

[165]

SUDDENLY FLOWERS IN THE MEADOW

A CHORAL READING BY AILEEN FISHER

Solo:

    In winter when the hills were bare,
    in winter when the fields were shorn
    and cold thrust daggers everywhere,
    a Child was born.

Chorus:

    Suddenly flowers in the meadow!
    Suddenly grass on the slope!
    Out of the cold and shadow
    flourished the green of hope.

Solo:

    In winter when the year was old
    and leafless branches stood forlorn
    and throats of winter birds were cold,
    a Child was born.

Chorus:

    Suddenly leaves on the branches!
    Suddenly birds to sing!
    Out of the dark and silence
    glistened the pledge of spring.

Solo:

    In winter when a star was high
    above a stable, weather-worn,
    and lowly creatures stood near-by,
    a Child was born.

Chorus:

    Suddenly light in the darkness,
    suddenly, clear and strong,
    out of the cold and starkness
    echoed an angel's song!

Solo:

In winter when the heart was sore,
in winter when the mind was torn
by bitter anguish to the core,
a Child was born.

Chorus:

Suddenly hope and gladness!
Suddenly faith's rebirth.
Out of despair and sadness,
peace, and good will on earth.

SING HEY!

UNKNOWN

Sing hey! Sing hey!
For Christmas Day;
Twine mistletoe and holly,
For friendship glows
In winter snows,
And so let's all be jolly!

THE TWELVE DAYS OF CHRISTMAS

UNKNOWN

The first day of Christmas,
My true love sent to me
A partridge in a pear tree.

The second day of Christmas,
My true love sent to me
Two turtle doves, and
A partridge in a pear tree.

The third day of Christmas,
My true love sent to me
Three French hens,
Two turtle doves, and
A partridge in a pear tree.

The fourth day of Christmas,
My true love sent to me
Four colly birds,
Three French hens,
Two turtle doves, and
A partridge in a pear tree.

The fifth day of Christmas,
My true love sent to me
Five gold rings,
Four colly birds,
Three French hens,
Two turtle doves, and
A partridge in a pear tree.

The sixth day of Christmas,
My true love sent to me
Six geese a-laying,
Five gold rings,
Four colly birds,
Three French hens,
Two turtle doves, and
A partridge in a pear tree.

The seventh day of Christmas,
My true love sent to me
Seven swans a-swimming,
Six geese a-laying,
Five gold rings,
Four colly birds,
Three French hens,
Two turtle doves, and
A partridge in a pear tree.

The eighth day of Christmas,
My true love sent to me
Eight maids a-milking,
Seven swans a-swimming,
Six geese a-laying,
Five gold rings,
Four colly birds,
Three French hens,
Two turtle doves, and
A partridge in a pear tree.

The ninth day of Christmas,
My true love sent to me
Nine drummers drumming,
Eight maids a-milking,
Seven swans a-swimming,
Six geese a-laying,
Five gold rings,
Four colly birds,
Three French hens,
Two turtle doves, and
A partridge in a pear tree.

The tenth day of Christmas,
My true love sent to me
Ten pipers piping,
Nine drummers drumming,
Eight maids a-milking,
Seven swans a-swimming,
Six geese a-laying,
Five gold rings,
Four colly birds,
Three French hens,
Two turtle doves, and
A partridge in a pear tree.

[170]

The eleventh day of Christmas,
My true love sent to me
Eleven ladies dancing,
Ten pipers piping,
Nine drummers drumming,
Eight maids a-milking,
Seven swans a-swimming,
Six geese a-laying,
Five gold rings,
Four colly birds,
Three French hens,
Two turtle doves, and
A partridge in a pear tree.

The twelfth day of Christmas,
My true love sent to me
Twelve fiddlers fiddling,
Eleven ladies dancing,
Ten pipers piping,
Nine drummers drumming,
Eight maids a-milking,
Seven swans a-swimming,
Six geese a-laying,
Five gold rings,
Four colly birds,
Three French hens,
Two turtle doves, and
A partridge in a pear tree.

A CHRISTMAS HYMN

BY CHRISTINA G. ROSSETTI

Love came down at Christmas,
Love all lovely, Love Divine;
Love was born at Christmas,
Star and Angels gave the sign.

Worship we the Godhead,
Love incarnate, Love Divine;
Worship we our Jesus:
But wherewith for sacred sign?

Love shall be our token,
Love be yours and love be mine,
Love to God and all men,
Love for plea and gift and sign.

THE OXEN

BY THOMAS HARDY

Christmas Eve, and twelve of the clock.
"Now they are all on their knees,"
An elder said as we sat in a flock
By the embers in hearthside ease.

We pictured the meek mild creatures where
They dwelt in their strawy pen,
Nor did it occur to one of us there
To doubt they were kneeling then.

So fair a fancy few would weave
In these years! Yet, I feel,
If someone said on Christmas Eve,
"Come; see the oxen kneel,

"In the lonely barton by yonder coomb
Our childhood used to know,"
I should go with him in the gloom,
Hoping it might be so.

[172]

MY GIFT

BY CHRISTINA G. ROSSETTI

What can I give Him
Poor as I am;
If I were a shepherd,
I would give Him a lamb.
If I were a wise man,
I would do my part.
But what can I give Him?
I will give Him my heart.

THE THREE KINGS

BY HENRY WADSWORTH LONGFELLOW

Three Kings came riding from far away,
    Melchior and Gaspar and Baltasar;
Three Wise Men out of the East were they,
And they travelled by night and they slept by day,
    For their guide was a beautiful, wonderful star.

The star was so beautiful, large, and clear,
    That all the other stars of the sky
Became a white mist in the atmosphere,
And by this they knew that the coming was near
    Of the Prince foretold in the prophecy.

Three caskets they bore on their saddlebows,
    Three caskets of gold with golden keys;
Their robes were of crimson silk with rows
Of bells and pomegranates and furbelows,
    Their turbans like blossoming almond-trees.

And so the Three Kings rode into the West,
    Through the dusk of night, over hill and dell,
And sometimes they nodded with beard on breast,
And sometimes talked, as they paused to rest,
    With the people they met at some wayside well.

"Of the child that is born," said Baltasar,
    "Good people, I pray you, tell us the news;
For we in the East have seen his star,
And have ridden fast, and have ridden far,
    To find and worship the King of the Jews."

And the people answered, "You ask in vain;
    We know of no king but Herod the Great!"
They thought the Wise Men were men insane,
As they spurred their horses across the plain,
    Like riders in haste, and who cannot wait.

And when they came to Jerusalem,
  Herod, the Great, who had heard this thing,
Sent for the Wise Men and questioned them;
And said, "Go down unto Bethlehem,
  And bring me tidings of this new king."

So they rode away; and the star stood still,
  The only one in the gray of morn;
Yes, it stopped,—it stood still of its own free will,
Right over Bethlehem on the hill,
  The city of David, where Christ was born.

And the Three Kings rode through the gate and the guard,
  Through the silent street, till their horses turned
And neighed as they entered the great inn yard;
But the windows were closed, and the doors were barred,
  And only a light in the stable burned.

And cradled there in the scented hay,
  In the air made sweet by the breath of kine,
The little child in the manger lay,
The child, that would be king one day
  Of a kingdom not human but divine.

His mother Mary of Nazareth
  Sat watching beside his place of rest,
Watching the even flow of his breath,
For the joy of life and the terror of death
  Were mingled together in her breast.

They laid their offerings at his feet:
  The gold was their tribute to a King,
The frankincense, with its odor sweet,
Was for the Priest, the Paraclete,
  The myrrh for the body's burying.

And the mother wondered and bowed her head,
  And sat as still as a statue of stone;
Her heart was troubled yet comforted,

Remembering what the Angel had said
  Of an endless reign and of David's throne.

Then the Kings rode out of the city gate,
  With a clatter of hoofs in proud array;
But they went not back to Herod the Great,
For they knew his malice and feared his hate,
  And returned to their homes by another way.

DISCARDED CHRISTMAS TREE

BY ELIZABETH-ELLEN LONG

Fall gently, rain, on leaf and limb
Which gave up growing just for Him.
Blow softly, wind, upon the tree
Which died for His nativity.

For though cast off by us, at will,
With no one caring, yet it still,
Of all green things remains the one
Which wore a Star for God's own Son!

POST-CHRISTMAS RHYME

BY RACHEL FIELD

Before the festive berries fall
  Like jeweled rain; before the tree
That stands in aromatic green
  Is stripped of shining finery;
Before the heart's high brimming cup
  Holds one drop less of fiery dew—
Pray God that all of us may keep
  One Christmas spark the whole year through.

CHRISTMAS
STORIES

The Little Blind Shepherd

Many years ago there lived a shepherd and his wife who had one child, a little boy; but they could not be happy because their son was blind. Thaddy had never seen either of them, nor had he seen the flowers of spring or the snows of winter. Now to Thaddy this was not strange, for he did not know or understand what seeing could be. But as he grew older he knew that he was missing something. But that *something* could not keep Thaddy from being happy. Sometimes he played in the meadows near home with his friends. But most often he liked to go into the hills with his father to tend the sheep.

On a certain day in the winter of the year, Thaddy was on his way up to the hills to join his father. Climbing higher and higher, he followed the footpaths he knew so well. As he neared the top, the wind whistled so strongly around his head that he had a hard time to catch his breath. He decided to lie down for a moment to rest. The tall grass was a protecting shield from the wind.

After a while he heard footsteps coming down the path, and presently he heard the voices of shepherds he had known for a long time. Thaddy was surprised to hear that they were talking about him.

"That blind son of Seth's will be a great burden to all of us, one day," grumbled the man whose name was Jethro.

"Thaddy will be as good a shepherd as any of our sons," said the other. Thaddy recognized him as Alban, his father's closest friend.

"But the day will come," insisted Jethro, "when the boy himself will be too old for herding. Then it will fall to the lot of one of our sons to feed and clothe him."

To this Alban replied, "Thaddy is a dear friend to our sons!"

Jethro grunted. "Friendship wears thin when it comes to bread and meat. That lad will be a beggar in the streets and will turn, more than likely, to stealing."

Thaddy could keep quiet no longer. "No, no!" he shouted, jumping up from his concealed place in the grass. "I will never be a thief!"

Jethro seized the boy by the arm. "Ha! You have been listening, have you?" the shepherd shouted. "And now you will say I have hurt your feelings. No more than you deserve! Little pitchers have big ears, I always say!"

"You have said more than enough," muttered Alban. He took Thaddy's hand. "Jethro does not mean what he said. We all know how honest you are."

Thaddy fought hard to keep from crying. "I'm sorry I listened, Alban. It was wrong, I know. Little pitchers *do* have big ears. But . . . it seems ears are all I have, Jethro. I promise you I will never listen again. And I promise you this, too: I will never steal!"

The little blind shepherd stumbled away, up the path, over the brow of the hill, and on to his father's grazing land. Now, Thaddy was not a talebearer and he did not tell his father what had been said. Instead, he began to think very seriously of what would become of him when he grew older.

As the days passed, Thaddy's parents, Seth and Sophira, worried about the sad and hopeless quiet that had fallen on the lad. At supper one evening Seth asked, "What is wrong, my son? No; don't turn away. Tell us why you no longer laugh and play with the other children."

Thaddy sighed. "I have been thinking what shall become of me when I am too old to be a shepherd in the hills. I must earn my fortune long before that, so I need never be a burden to anyone."

Sophira patted the little blind one's shoulder. "That day is many years away," she said softly.

But Thaddy insisted. "I must start soon. If only I had two or three she-goats! The Roman soldiers at the garrison in town like goat milk, and I could sell it to them." Here at last, Thaddy smiled, thinking of his plan. "With the money I earned from the goat milk—I know it would take a long time to earn it—with that money, I could buy a cart and donkey to haul vegetables into the market place. I could plant the fields and be a farmer-shepherd, until I should grow too old. But by that time, I'd have a fortune and no one would think me a burden!"

Thaddy sounded so sure of his plan that his parents sat quietly a moment. Then Seth asked, "And you could accomplish all this with three she-goats?"

"Oh, yes, Father, I feel sure I could," Thaddy replied. "The goats could graze among the sheep, and would be no trouble at all."

"Can we afford to buy the goats, Seth?" asked Sophira.

Seth rubbed his beard a moment, then said, "I think it might be possible. Sleep well tonight, Thaddy, and you and I will go into the market tomorrow."

The next morning found Thaddy and his father in the noisy market place, where they bought the three goats Thaddy chose. How proud he was to drive them home, then up into the hillside pastures!

At sunset, he was home again, working out his plan.

"If the Roman soldiers will buy the milk from me—and I am sure they will—I can save enough money to buy a donkey and cart. Only one thing worries me," Thaddy admitted to his mother. "How do you milk a goat?"

Sophira laughed, a silvery, happy sound. "Your father will show you."

[181]

And Thaddy learned easily how to milk the goats. He had collected several earthen jugs and they were soon filled with his first day's milking.

Early in the morning he found his way to the garrison of Roman soldiers stationed near Bethlehem. A sergeant, meeting Thaddy at the gate, asked, "What does the young citizen want of his Roman protectors? Are you lost?"

"Oh, no; I am never lost," answered Thaddy. "I have heard that the Roman soldiers delight in drinking goat's milk. I seek permission to sell them the milk of my goats. You will find that it is clean and fresh. Please, will you not taste it?"

The sergeant took the jug Thaddy handed to him. He poured a little of the milk into a silver cup which was fastened to his belt. Then, slowly, he drank the milk while Thaddy waited. "Best I've had in many a month!" he announced. "But—are you sure you didn't steal it?"

Thaddy shook his head. "I will never steal. I want to earn my living and save enough money for my old age, so that I shall never have to beg or steal."

"Come in," said the sergeant, as he touched Thaddy's elbow to lead him through the gate. "Our soldiers will be your good customers. Shall I lead you to them? I see you are blind."

"Just this once," was Thaddy's reply. "Then I shall know the way."

The sergeant led Thaddy to a row of tents and stopped before the first one. "Bartus!" he called. "Here is a young Judean merchant come to sell his wares. Do you want to buy some goat's milk?"

Thaddy heard Bartus snap back the tent flap. "Milk? Indeed, I will gladly buy from such a young merchant! Will you come by every day, sightless one?"

"If I may be permitted, Bartus."

Another hand reached for Thaddy's elbow. "Come into the tent, lad! Men, up with your measures, if you would drink fresh milk!"

Then Bartus added, "Pay the boy generously if you wish him to come back again."

Cup after cup clinked against the sides of Thaddy's jugs. In a short time, they were emptied, and the boy hurried home, jingling his Roman coins. He had made a start in his business venture.

Through the months, Thaddy faithfully carried his goat milk to the Roman soldiers and gave his mother every copper he earned. Finally, within a year, Thaddy managed to buy a little donkey and cart. But how stubborn the little donkey was!

One morning at sun-up, Thaddy tried to back his animal into the cart traces. It was a job that exhausted his patience, and Thaddy scolded. "I shall call you Petra. In the Roman language it means rock. That is exactly what you are, when you set your feet! Now"—and here Thaddy began to coax—"why won't you let me hitch you to the cart? We must take the milk to our soldier friends, then go to the market place in Bethlehem. If we are late, we shall not get a good price for these things we have dug from the garden."

All this time Sophira had been standing in the doorway, watching. "You must have more patience, my son," she said. "A sleepy little donkey does not want to work so early. If you will but speak softly to him, he will do your bidding."

Thaddy tightened the last buckle. "I will try to remember, Mother," he promised. "We will be careful. I shall walk at Petra's side in the city streets."

The little blind shepherd led his donkey down the road to the Roman garrison where his friend, the sergeant, was watching and waiting for him.

"Good morning!" Thaddy sang out, when he knew he was close to the garrison gate. "I have brought you some turnips from my garden!"

"Good morning, Thaddy; thanks for the turnips," replied the sergeant. "It is a beautiful day. All Judea shimmers in the bright sun. I wish you could stand here and see what I see: the city, spread out, all white and clean, with not a cloud in the sky." The sergeant breathed a deep breath, then chuckled. "Except possibly one. We have just received a decree from Caesar Augustus that all men should be taxed. Our governor, Cyrenius, says every man must go to his home city to register and pay tax. But the day for tax paying is in the cold months, when the snow is on the ground. It will be hard for some."

But Thaddy's face lighted up at the news. He had an uncle, his mother's brother David, who now lived in Nazareth and was an importer of silks and spices. Thaddy asked the sergeant if the decree meant that Uncle David would come to visit.

The sergeant laughed. "If he obeys the law, he will! It seems there is a bright side to every cloud. Will you be happy to see your uncle?"

"Oh, yes!" Thaddy assured him. "Uncle David is a merchant who does business with traders from the Orient, and he brings spices and sweet oils and other presents when he comes to visit us. I am glad you have told me such good news!"

"Your uncle may not consider it good news," said the Roman. "A journey in the cold months is far from pleasant."

Thaddy's face clouded as he kicked the dust at his feet. "Can you tell me," he asked, "why the day for tax paying is so late in the year? Is it because we are—a conquered people?"

"Perhaps," replied the sergeant, trying to sound lighthearted, "although the governor Cyrenius explains that he is allowing three months for everyone to gather together his tax money."

Thaddy thought a moment; then he said, "That seems good and kind. Anyway, my mother will be happy. She does not see Uncle David very often. But Sergeant, do you know where Petra and I are going today? Down into the market! See all the vegetables I have, fresh from my garden!"

The Roman, thinking how much Thaddy was like his own son, put his arm around the little blind boy. "You are a good worker, Thaddy. Leave the milk with me. I will collect your money for it from the soldiers, and you can stop for it on your way home from the market."

So Thaddy and Petra went off to the market in Bethlehem, where soon was heard Thaddy's cry: "Turnips and peas, grown in the shade of the olive trees! Fresh-picked this morning! Turnips and peas!"

Thaddy found ready customers for his wares that day and all through the season. Then the last of his crops was sold, and winter descended on the hills and valleys of Judea. Even then, he appeared quite often to sell cheeses he had made from goat's milk. Snow fell, making the road from Nazareth to Bethlehem hard to travel, but sure-footed Petra seemed to enjoy the journey more than ever.

One bitter, snowy afternoon as Thaddy and Petra neared home, Thaddy heard, through the howling winds, voices just ahead on the road.

"Just a little farther, Mary," urged a man's voice.

"But I can not walk, even a little farther," came the woman's reply. "My feet ache with the cold. Surely there is an inn close at hand?"

"I will carry you, pretty one," said the man.

Thaddy called out into the storm. "Is the lady sick? Can I help you?" Thaddy came close to the strangers. "My home is near here. Will you come with me and be warmed before going on your way?"

"You are very kind, my son," replied the woman, "but we must reach Bethlehem before dark."

Thaddy felt his heart and sympathy going out toward the woman in the storm. "Let me give you my donkey," he said eagerly. "My cart is not comfortable enough for the sick lady. We can leave it by the side of the road. It is empty."

Tired as she was, the woman smiled. "Bless you, little one," she said, "your parents would be angry if you came home without your donkey."

"But I would tell them," Thaddy insisted, "that I gave Petra to a sweet-sounding lady. They will understand!"

The lady drew in a quick breath. "Joseph," she said, "this boy is blind. Is it right to accept his kindness?"

The man's voice came quietly, "Perhaps it is a sign." Then, to Thaddy he added, "Tell us your name, son. We shall be coming back this way in a few days, and will return your donkey to you. Many thanks to you for your kind mercy to Mary, my wife."

Thaddy quickly unbuckled the straps that held Petra to the cart. "May I help you up onto Petra's back?" he asked. Mary saw him lace his fingers together, so she put her foot lightly into his hands as Joseph lifted her to Petra's back. Now Thaddy stood back and urged them on to Bethlehem. "Good-bye, Petra," he called against the wind. "Be very good for the lady. Walk as gently as you can!"

As he heard Joseph and Mary go off into the storm, Thaddy turned and hurried home. These were familiar footpaths, and it was not long before he arrived.

Warmth, and the smells of good things cooking, flooded over the blind boy as his father helped him out of his coat. "You have been so long coming home," Seth scolded, "that your mother was beginning to worry. She has a surprise for you."

Thaddy hung his coat on its peg. "A surprise for me? What is it, Mother?" Sophira held a little box close to Thaddy's nose. "It's—sandalwood!" the boy sang out. "Uncle David is here! When did you arrive, Uncle David?"

"This morning, just after you left for market," Uncle David said, stepping out of the shadow of the cupboard. He had forgotten that one need not hide from blind boys. "I have waited all day to see my nephew. Your mother and father tell me you are a businessman, now."

"I have earned over a hundred pieces of Roman silver," Thaddy reported proudly. "Mother has saved the money for me, and I shall buy more goats when spring comes. My milk and cheese sell very well."

Now Uncle David rumpled Thaddy's hair. "You must show me your investment. I have heard great things about your donkey and cart."

Thaddy smiled. "I can't do that, Uncle David," he answered; then he added, "I do not have Petra any longer. I gave him to a poor man and his wife who were traveling in the storm."

Uncle David's hand slipped from Thaddy's shoulder, and his voice held disbelief as he exclaimed, "You gave your donkey away? I knew I had a blind nephew, but certainly not a foolish one."

Thaddy's mother tried to explain that Petra was Thaddy's donkey, to give or keep as he chose, but Uncle David shouted angrily, "You uphold him, Sophira? I *am* surprised! It was my intention to leave my blind nephew well-fixed when I go from this world. But when I see how little he cares for what belongs to him—!" Thaddy was frightened by his uncle's rage, and he struggled to get away, but Uncle David's strong hands were clutching Thaddy's shoulders. "What's to become of you, Nephew, if you are senseless at your age?"

Seth, Thaddy's father, took the boy into his arms and said quietly, "Thaddy will never need your money, David. Perhaps it is best for you to go to your bed. You will have a hard day with the Roman tax collectors tomorrow." Thaddy listened to Uncle David walking, without a word, from the room. Then he heard his father say, "I'm sorry, Sophira. I know how you enjoy David's visits, and I should not quarrel with him, but . . . I must go up to build fires to keep the sheep warm. The night is too cold for them."

Hearing this, Thaddy begged, "Take me with you, Father. I can coax the sheep close to the fires. They trust me."

Seth looked to Sophira for an answer, and when she nodded, he said simply, "Put on your heavy coat, son. Your mother will give us something to eat, because we shall be gone a good part of the night. If you smile, she may give us some of the little cakes you like."

[187]

It took just a moment for Thaddy to throw his heavy coat over his shoulders, and in a little while he and Seth were climbing the cold, rocky path to the grazing sheep. The storm had stopped, the night was clear, and every star shone bright, reaching down from the blue night sky. As Seth started the first fire, Thaddy asked timidly, "You are not angry with me because I gave Petra to the strangers? Was I foolish, Father?"

Seth's laugh rang in the night air. "No, Thaddy! Only generous. Now that one fire is blazing, you can bring the young sheep, and the old ones will follow. I will build another fire near Alban and Jethro's flocks."

"Are they not in the hills with their sheep?"

"Oh, yes," Seth answered, "they are here. But Jethro thinks a fire is a foolish waste of wood. He thinks *I* am too generous when I build a fire."

In the flickering firelight, Seth saw a troubled look twist his son's face. He waited for Thaddy's question. "Will you ask them to come and eat with us? I have not been friendly to Jethro for over a year. But, tonight is different, somehow. I—I can't explain it. Tonight, it seems good to be friendly. Besides," he added, "Alban is jolly, and will make us forget the cold."

"I will ask them," Seth promised.

Thaddy made his way among the sheep, careful not to stumble. It would not do to show Uncle David a broken leg, he thought. The goats and sheep knew Thaddy, and they followed him readily. It seemed no time at all until he heard Alban, Jethro, and Seth coming along the path.

"And how is our young merchant?" Alban called out. "We do not see you very often, these days, Thaddy. Is your fortune growing?"

"One hundred and eight pieces of Roman silver, not counting what I brought home today," was Thaddy's reply.

Alban chuckled. "He's a sharp one, this son of yours, Seth. While all of us pay tax to the Romans, he has them paying him."

Thaddy heard Jethro join in the laughter. Perhaps Jethro wasn't angry with him any more. Perhaps he felt, too, that this was a good night to be friendly. Now Jethro began to talk, and Thaddy caught up with his words. "What I want to know, Seth, is whether it is good to mix sheep and goats in the same pasture. At first, I was against goats in these hills, but since the lad has been successful——"

Seth interrupted, saying, "A good shepherd can always separate sheep from goats, when he has to," and Jethro was about to reply when Alban called out, "Seth! What is this bright light overhead?" At this, Jethro moaned in great fear and Alban gasped, "What strange thing is this?"

Thaddy put out his hand but could reach no one. "Father," he cried, "why is every one afraid?"

Seth, remembering that at times like this he must be Thaddy's eyes, said, "There is a great white light, and in its center, an angel of the Lord. I, too, am afraid, Thaddy."

The night air was filled with the tinkling of tiny bells, and the angel said, "Fear not . . . For behold, I bring you tidings of great joy, which shall be to all people."

"Can you hear him, Father?" Thaddy whispered. "The angel will not harm us. Tell Alban and Jethro not to run away."

Again the angel spoke. "For unto you is born this day, in the City of David, a Saviour, which is Christ the Lord."

Thaddy no longer crouched among the frightened shepherds; he wanted so much to know about the Saviour that he could not help asking, "But how shall we find the Saviour? How can we know where he is?"

"This shall be a sign unto you. Ye shall find the Babe wrapped in swaddling clothes, lying in a manger." And suddenly, there was with the angel a multitude of the heavenly host, praising God, and saying, "Glory to God in the highest! And on earth peace, good will toward men!" With a rush of heavenly music, the brightness of the angels dissolved into a bright and glittering star which stood over one portion of the city of Bethlehem.

Alban, still shaken by what he had seen, held out his hands to his friends and said, "Seth . . . Jethro . . . Let us now go, even unto Bethlehem, and see this thing which is come to pass."

"We must certainly go," Seth agreed. "There is some great reason why we have been chosen to learn these glad tidings."

Jethro, impatient as always, urged them to make haste, since the star might fade, and they not find the Saviour. When Thaddy pleaded to go with them, Jethro blurted out "No! The lad will stumble, Seth, and make our progress slow. Send him home."

Thaddy's heart sank. Could they really deny him the magic of the night, when he was sure, so sure, that the angel had spoken especially to him?

But Seth insisted, saying "This is Thaddy's heritage. He felt it this night, when he asked me to bring you to our fire. You are welcome to go ahead. I shall walk with Thaddy." Seth put his arm across Thaddy's shoulders, and held him close.

Immediately, Jethro's voice softened. "No . . . We shall go together. I spoke too quickly, as I have always done."

Down the paths they hurried, then along the road past the sleeping Roman garrison, a way so familiar to Thaddy that he knew they were near the city.

It was Alban's voice that broke the long silence. "The bright star hangs over an inn. How shall we ever find the Child, without rousing the whole inn?"

Thaddy recalled that the angel had said they would find the Baby lying in a manger, and when they had come to the inn; they inquired of the innkeeper's wife where a Child had been born that night.

The good woman went on wiping the crumbs from the table as she replied to their questions. "You have heard of it so soon? The poor little mother! We had no room for them in the inn, so many people have come to pay their taxes! But I could not send her away." The innkeeper's wife placed the lamp carefully in the center of the table, and pulled the wick up a little. Thaddy heard her voice grow soft and kind. "She rode a little donkey, and was so worn by her journey . . . I took her and her husband to the stable, where it is warmer than most rooms in the inn. And in no time at all, the dear little Child was born."

The innkeeper's wife looked more closely at Thaddy. "Why . . . You are the little blind fellow who sells in the market. I have bought from you, many a time."

"Yes, I remember," said Thaddy. "But—don't you know?" he asked. "The Baby is the Saviour of the world. An angel told us."

Alban stepped forward and said, "Do not doubt the boy. What he says is true. And we have come to see this wonderful thing that has occurred."

At this, the innkeeper's wife frowned. She thought it would be kinder to let the mother and father rest. "I was with Mary no more than half an hour ago, and she had just wrapped the Babe in swaddling clothes, and laid Him in the manger." As she spoke, the door swung open, and in its shadow stood a man.

"I am sorry to disturb you, good woman," said the man. "The Babe sleeps, and Mary feels she can eat some porridge and milk."

The innkeeper's wife smiled. "Oh, it's you, Joseph. I will warm the porridge right away," she promised. "Come out of the shadows. These are shepherds who have come to see the Child."

Thaddy was trying to remember. Had he heard the man's voice before now? But more than that, he wanted to explain why they had come, and his words tumbled out hurriedly. "An angel told us the Babe is the Saviour all Judea has waited for, these many generations."

Then Joseph spoke to him. "Aren't you the boy who gave his donkey so that Mary's journey might be easier?" Thaddy made no reply, and Seth explained that his son was blind, and could recognize people only by their voices. "Then he is the boy. Come with me," Joseph said, taking Thaddy's hand and beckoning the shepherds to follow him.

Thaddy put his hand trustingly into Joseph's, and the shepherds followed them into the starlit courtyard, past the well, and on to the stable, where Joseph swung open the door.

"The Child sleeps," he whispered, "but Mary will be glad to see you. Come in." As they entered, he spoke gently to his wife. "Mary, some shepherds have come to see the Child. They know who He is, Mary."

The little blind shepherd was delighted when he heard Mary speak. "All shall be fulfilled, as the angel has told me." She was truly the lady in the storm! Now she was saying "Come close. I will lift away the blanket." The shepherds crowded round the sleeping Child. "Ah! How good He looks," exclaimed Alban. "I shall remember Him always."

But would they never remember little blind Thaddy? At last, he begged, "Please, Lady . . . I am blind. I can not see the Child. May I touch Him, so that I may remember Him, too?"

Mary's eyes fell on the lad and glowed with recognition. "Joseph! This is the blind boy who was so good to us!" To Thaddy, she said, "Truly you shall be blessed, lad. Reach out your arms. I will let you hold my Son. . . . Gently . . . We must not disturb His slumber."

Then Thaddy felt the slight weight of the Baby across his arms. And as he held the precious bundle to his heart, the world grew bright and warm for Thaddy. The light became form, the form took shape, and the shape was the Christ Child, lying peacefully in Thaddy's arms.

When at last Thaddy could speak, he cried out, "Lady! I can see Him! With my eyes! I do not understand, but . . . I can see Him, Lady!"

In a moment Seth was on his knees beside his son. He bowed his head to the floor of the stable.

"Let us give thanks to God and to this holy Child," he murmured. "My son Thaddy sees for the first time in his life. Oh, little Babe in the manger, may you be as good to the rest of the world as you are to my Thaddy." Seth got to his feet. "Now we must hasten to tell his mother the wondrous thing that has happened."

As they turned to go, Joseph put his hand on Seth's shoulder. "Will you take the donkey with you? Your son was very kind to us."

Thaddy saw the question light his father's eyes, and he knew he must speak for himself. "I think you will need Petra, Joseph," he said. "Besides, I should like to think that he is serving the Child, even as He has served me."

Outside the stable, dawn was breaking, all blue and pink and gold for Thaddy. And the shepherds went their way, praising God for all the things that they had heard and seen.

BY GEORGE SHARP

GIFTS FOR THE FIRST BIRTHDAY

It was winter—and twelve months since the gipsies had driven their flocks of mountain-sheep over the dark, gloomy Balkans, and had settled in the southlands near to the Ægean. It was twelve months since they had seen a wonderful star appear in the sky and heard the singing of angelic voices afar off.

They had marveled much concerning the star until a runner had passed them from the South bringing them news that the star had marked the birth of a Child whom the wise men had hailed as "King of Israel" and "Prince of Peace." This had made Herod of Judea both afraid and angry and he had sent soldiers secretly to kill the Child; but in the night they had miraculously disappeared—the Child with Mary and Joseph—and no one knew whither they had gone. Therefore Herod had sent runners all over the lands that bordered the Mediterranean with a message forbidding every one giving food or shelter or warmth to the Child, under penalty of death. For Herod's anger was far-reaching and where his anger fell there fell his sword likewise. Having given his warning, the runner passed on, leaving the gipsies to marvel much over the tale they had heard and the meaning of the star.

Now on that day that marked the end of the twelve months since the star had shone the gipsies said among themselves: "Dost thou think that the star will shine again to-night? If it were true, what the runner said, that when it shone twelve months ago it marked the place where the Child lay it may even mark His hiding-place this night. Then Herod would know where to find Him, and send his soldiers again to slay Him. That would be a cruel thing to happen!"

The air was chill with the winter frost, even there in the south-land, close to the Ægean; and the gipsies built high their fire and hung their kettle full of millet, fish, and bitter herbs for their supper. The king lay on his couch of tiger-skins and on his arms were amulets of heavy gold, while rings of gold were on his fingers and in his ears. His tunic was of heavy silk covered with a leopard cloak, and on his feet were shoes of goatskin trimmed with fur. Now, as they feasted around the fire a voice came to them through the darkness, calling. It was a man's voice, climbing the mountains from the south.

"Ohe! Ohe!" he shouted. And then nearer, "O—he!"

The gipsies were still disputing among themselves whence the voice came when there walked into the circle about the fire a tall, shaggy man, grizzled with age, and a sweet-faced young mother carrying a child.

"We are outcasts," said the man, hoarsely. "Ye must know that whosoever succors us will bring Herod's vengeance like a sword about his head. For a year we have wandered homeless and cursed over the world. Only the wild creatures have not feared to share their food and give us shelter in their lairs. But to-night we can go no farther; and we beg the warmth of your fire and food enough to stay us until the morrow."

The king looked at them long before he made reply. He saw the weariness in their eyes and the famine in their cheeks; he saw, as well, the holy light that hung about the child, and he said at last to his men:

"It is the Child of Bethlehem, the one they call the 'Prince of Peace.' As yon man says, who shelters them shelters the wrath of Herod as well. Shall we let them tarry?"

One of their number sprang to his feet, crying: "It is a sin to turn strangers from the fire, a greater sin if they be poor and friendless. And what is a king's wrath to us? I say bid them welcome. What say the rest?"

And with one accord the gipsies shouted, "Yea, let them tarry!"

They brought fresh skins and threw them down beside the fire for the man and woman to rest on. They brought them food and wine, and goat's milk for the Child; and when they had seen that all was made comfortable for them they gathered round the Child—these black gipsy men—to touch His small white hands and feel His golden hair. They brought Him a chain of gold to play with and another for His neck and tiny arm.

"See, these shall be Thy gifts, little one," said they, "the gifts for Thy first birthday."

And long after all had fallen asleep the Child lay on His bed of skins beside the blazing fire and watched the light dance on the beads of gold. He laughed and clapped His hands together to see the pretty sight they made; and then a bird called out of the thicket close by.

"Little Child of Bethlehem," it called, "I, too, have a birth gift for Thee. I will sing Thy cradle song this night." And softly, like the tinkling of a silver bell and like clear water running over mossy places, the nightingale sang and sang, filling the air with melodies.

And then another voice called to Him:

"Little Child of Bethlehem, I am only a tree with boughs all bare, for the winter has stolen my green cloak, but I also can give Thee a birth gift. I can give Thee shelter from the biting north wind that blows." And the tree bent low its branches and twined a rooftree and a wall about the Child.

Soon the Child was fast asleep, and while He slept a small brown bird hopped out of the thicket. Cocking his little head, he said:

"What can I be giving the Child of Bethlehem? I could fetch Him a fat worm to eat or catch Him the beetle that crawls on yonder bush, but He would not like that! And I could tell Him a story of the lands of the north, but He is asleep and would not hear." And the brown bird shook its head quite sorrowfully. Then it saw that the wind was bringing the sparks from the fire nearer and nearer to the sleeping Child.

"I know what I can do," said the bird, joyously. "I can catch the hot sparks on my breast, for if one should fall upon the Child it would burn Him grievously."

So the small brown bird spread wide his wings and caught the sparks on his own brown breast. So many fell that the feathers were burned; and burned was the flesh beneath until the breast was no longer brown, but red.

Next morning, when the gipsies awoke, they found Mary and Joseph and the Child gone. For Herod had died, and an angel had come in the night and carried them back to the land of Judea. But the good God blessed those who had cared that night for the Child.

To the nightingale He said: "Your song shall be the sweetest in all the world, for ever and ever; and only you shall sing the long night through."

To the tree He said: "Little fir-tree, never more shall your branches be bare. Winter and summer you and your seedlings shall stay green, ever green."

Last of all He blessed the brown bird: "Faithful little watcher, from this night forth you and your children shall have red breasts, that the world may never forget your gift to the Child of Bethlehem."

BY RUTH SAWYER

[197]

Simon, the crippled child, often leaned out of his window to see the Boy pass. The street was narrow and flooded with the clear light of the Nazarene sun, except where the shadows of houses threw arabesques of shade across the way. The Boy was going down the street now. Simon looked down, and the Boy, feeling his gaze, looked up and smiled.

"Peace be with you!" he called gaily, giving the customary greeting.

"Peace be with you," returned Simon, seriously, but he wished the Boy would stop, open the wide door leading to his house, and come up and talk to him. He had so few friends among children, and while his father was a well-to-do merchant and gave him everything his heart desired, he longed for a lively companion of his own age.

For weeks now he had watched the Boy come and go in the street beneath his window. There was something about the Boy that fascinated and attracted him. His appearance was not unusual, save for a strangely beautiful expression of his face. He ran and laughed and shouted with other boys, yet there was something about him that caused him to stand out in Simon's mind. Simon, himself, could not say what it was.

One day Simon remembered hearing a great shouting and laughing going on in the street below. On looking out he had seen a crowd of boys chasing a wounded bird that hopped awkwardly about in a terrified endeavor to escape them. One of its wings had evidently been broken and it cried out pitifully, "Peep, peep! Peep, peep!"

The more the bird fluttered and cried, the more eager the boys became to catch it. Just as one of them seized it the Boy had come running up. Making a frantic effort, the bird escaped from his captor's fingers and half-fell, half-fluttered to the ground at the Boy's feet.

"There! Catch him! Now we've got him. Here, he's mine, I saw him first. Quick now, don't let him get away again!" shouted the others, and quarreling and yelling they surrounded the Boy.

Simon had a wonderful view from his window and he watched intently as the Boy, paying no attention to the clamoring children, reached down and picked up the bird. He held it between his two palms for a moment and spoke softly to it. Simon had not been able to catch his words above the tumult.

But, as the angry children surged about the Boy, demanding the bird as their rightful prey, Simon saw the Boy open his hands and free the bird that, miraculously, flew away.

For a moment the crowd of children were dumb with surprise, then one of the boys, evidently the leader, shouted:

"He let the bird go! It was none of his business. He is always doing those things. Here, let him have it!" Seizing a stone he hurled it at the Boy, who only laughed, and turned and ran on his swift, strong legs down the street.

Perhaps if Simon had himself been able to run and catch birds he would not have been so impressed by what he had seen, but as it was he had never forgotten it. The memory came back to him clearly today, as the Boy stood smiling up at him. Then, as though the Boy had read Simon's thoughts he said, "I will come back and visit with you on my way home if you want. I have to go on an errand now."

"Oh, please do stop," cried Simon delighted. "I have wanted to talk to you for a long time."

So the Boy went on his way whistling.

Now it happened that this was a feast day and Simon's father came to him, after their noonday meal, and said, "My son, soon you will be twelve years old, and today is a sacred day, so your mother and I would like to get you a present, something you most desire." The merchant smiled, and laid his hand on Simon's thin shoulder caressingly.

Simon looked up quickly into his father's face, and remembering how the Boy's strong legs had looked running down the street, he said, "Oh, Father, there is nothing in all the world I want except to run, to run down the street through the sunshine and out into the hills I can see from my window!"

The merchant turned his head away, and for a moment he could not speak, and when he did there was bitterness in his voice.

"And that wish, my son, is the one thing I cannot grant you," he said sadly.

Meanwhile, the Boy hurried on down the street, so that he would have time to visit with Simon awhile before his mother expected him back home. He remembered now that he had felt Simon watching him the day he had rescued the bird from the crowd of children. He had almost forgotten that experience. It did not seem strange to him that the bird had been able to fly away after he had picked it up. Things like that were always happening to him. He had never seen things like that happen to his playmates.

He had passed through the town now and was out in the beautiful countryside. His errand was with a shepherd, so he climbed up the steep hillside to find him. As he climbed, he breathed in the sweet, warm air. How beautiful the world was—how glad and happy he felt! He reached down and picked up a lamb that lay in the grass near its mother. Neither the ewe nor the lamb protested. The Boy petted the pretty creature and laid his cheek against its soft head.

"Little brother," he whispered, "dear little brother!"

Then, feeling a little breathless from his climb, he threw himself down on the soft hillside to rest. He let the lamb go, but it made no effort to return to its mother; instead, it lay peacefully beside him.

He looked down at the steep pathway where he had just ascended; violets bloomed in the path. The Boy was surprised; they had not bloomed there a few moments before. Well, no matter, things like that were always happening to him.

He looked about him at the splendid view he loved so well.

And to the south, far beyond the mountains and across the plains, lay the Holy City of Jerusalem.

Something stirred in his heart and urged him on. A kind of restlessness passed over him and was gone, as though someone was urging him to do something—something that lay half-sleeping in his memory, something he had once known and forgotten. It was often so lately; he meant to ask his mother about this strange feeling one day.

Suddenly his attention was arrested by the sight of one of those desperate struggles with which nature is replete. A ferret ran almost across his feet in pursuit of a fat young rabbit, wild with fright. It seemed to have no sense of direction and, at the sight of the Boy, doubled in its tracks and ran full into the ferret who immediately laid hold upon the little rabbit and began his kill.

The Boy jumped up and ran to the two struggling little creatures. He laid his hand upon the ferret who immediately released the rabbit and ran up the Boy's arm to perch like a squirrel upon his shoulder; while the rabbit, bleeding and quivering, crept into the Boy's shirt and lay there panting.

After playing with the two animals for a few minutes, the Boy placed them on the ground. In a minute the ferret disappeared to continue his hunt by night, and the rabbit hopped away into the underbrush, leaving no trail of blood behind him. The Boy laughed happily and ran on to find the shepherd to whom he had been told to deliver a message from his father, the carpenter.

The afternoon sun was low as the Boy started down the hill, and he knew it would soon slip out of sight behind Mount Carmel. He had stayed talking with the shepherd longer than he should, so he hurried; for he had not forgotten his promise to stop and visit awhile with Simon, the crippled boy. He wondered vaguely why people called Simon "crippled"; he appeared to him to look like any other boy in Nazareth.

In his arms the Boy carried the little lamb he had played with on the hillside; the shepherd had given it to him to take home to his father in payment of a debt. The Boy meant to ask his father if he could have the lamb for his own pet.

At last he reached Simon's house and, opening the street door, he called out, "Hello, Simon, I have come to talk to you. See what I have brought down from the hills!"

"Hello!" called Simon joyously. "Come on up the stairs; I have been waiting for you all afternoon."

So the Boy ran up the stairs and entered the room where the little cripple sat among his silk cushions on a couch.

Once inside the room, the Boy stopped and stared, overcome by its richness and splendor. For his own house was plain and dark, with barely enough for their needs. But as he stood still looking at Simon, sitting helpless amidst all this beauty, compassion swept over him like a great wave and his heart was full.

He looked deep into Simon's face; then he said, "Come, and see what I have brought; it is a little lamb from the hills."

Simon looked at the Boy in wonder and some embarrassment. "But I cannot walk," he said quietly.

Then the Boy put the lamb down, and running across the room he said, "Come, arise, I will help you walk."

And slowly, awkwardly, moving as in a trance, and holding fast to the Boy's strong brown hand, Simon rose from his couch and together the two boys walked across the room to where the little lamb stood bleating faintly.

"But I cannot walk," repeated Simon, dazedly.

The Boy laughed, and a great warmth entered into Simon. "Of course you can walk," said the Boy, "you can walk and run as well as any other boy in Nazareth! You can see, as I see, the hills and the plains and the blue violets springing up in the paths. Be ready, Simon, and tomorrow we shall go up into the hills together." The Boy stopped and turned his radiant face toward the opening door.

The merchant entered the room. At first he did not seem to see Simon standing near the Boy and, when he did, he stood dumb with surprise. Could this be Simon, his only son, crippled since birth?

Simon, himself, answered his father.

"Look, oh, look! Father, I can walk, I can run! He made me so!" And Simon ran across the room and threw himself, sobbing with joy, into his father's arms.

Quietly the Boy passed them and went down the stairs and out into the street. The swift dusk had already fallen. As he hurried toward his home he felt again that strange urging, that strange pulling at something sleeping in his mind. "Soon I shall be twelve," he told himself. "And then I shall go with Mother and Father to celebrate the Feast of the Passover in Jerusalem."

Softly he passed out of the dusk into the quiet comfort of his home. Already his mother and father and brothers were gathered about the table for the evening meal.

His mother looked up and smiled. "I am so glad you have come," she said. "I was worried."

The Boy smiled, too, but he made a strange answer.

"Soon I must be upon my way," he said.

In Simon's home the merchant was beside himself with joy and consternation. Carefully, he questioned Simon concerning the Boy. But Simon knew little, save that the Boy was the son of a humble carpenter, and that he frequently saw him run down the street and out in the direction of the hills.

"But what is his name?" persisted the merchant.

Simon thought a moment, then he said, "His name is Jesus."

BY EMILIE E. KING

The boy sat quiet alone on the hilltop, his shepherd's crook across his knees, his small square lunch basket beside him. He made an odd, distorted shadow in the white light of the moon, for even the fringed shawl that his mother had woven of lamb's wool could not hide the ugly hump that lay—a burden much too heavy for so young a lad to bear—between his shoulders.

Far below him, dotting the hillside with other irregular shadows, were the sheep. The majority of them slept, but a few wandered aimlessly up and down the slope. The boy, however, was not watching the flock. His head was thrown back, and his wide eyes were fixed on the sky.

"Perhaps it will happen again," he was thinking, "perhaps—though a third of a century has gone by. Perhaps I shall see the great star and hear the angel voices as my father did!"

The moon, riding high in the heavens, went under a blanket of cloud. For a moment the world was dark. The boy sighed and lowered his eyes.

"It is an omen," he breathed, "an omen! Though it is the time of anniversary, there will be no star this night. Neither will the angels sing . . ."

The time of anniversary. How often the boy had listened to the story of the miracle that had taken place so long ago! The boy's father had been a lad himself then—he had been the youngest of the shepherds on that glorious occasion when an angel anthem sounded across the world and a star shone above the tranquil town of Bethlehem. The boy's father had followed the star; with the other shepherds he had come to the stable of the inn. Crowding through the narrow doorway, he had seen a woman with a baby in her arms.

"But—" the boy's father had told the story so many times that his family and the neighbors knew it word for word—"she was no ordinary woman! There was something in her face that made one think of a lighted candle. And there was a tenderness in her smile that the very cattle felt, for they drew close to her and seemed to kneel. It was not her beauty, although beauty she did possess! It was a shine from within——"

"And the baby—" the boy always prompted his father here—*"what of the baby?"*

The father's hand touched his small son's shoulder at this point —touched it, and drew away.

"The baby," he said, and his voice grew hushed, "was as unlike other infants as his mother was different from other women. Scarce

an hour old when first I glimpsed him, there was a sense of wisdom—no, do not laugh—on his brow, and his tiny up-curled hands seemed—indeed, I do mean it!—to hold power. I found myself kneeling, as the cattle knelt, and there was the damp of tears upon my face, and—though I was a lad tall for my age—I was not ashamed."

Alone on the hillside the boy could almost hear the sound of his father's voice in the stillness. His father's voice telling the story of the marvelous infant and of the Wise Men who had come to the stable—following, also, in the path of the star. They had come bearing gifts, the fame of which traveled through all the land. Often the boy had heard of the gold and frankincense and myrrh; often he had shivered at the tale of the great cruel king who had ordered death to all male infants. Often he had thrilled to the saga of a worried young mother—and her sober husband—who had stolen away into the land of Egypt with her child.

"Many of us thought," the boy's father finished, "that the child had been captured and slain by Herod. Until a decade passed and we heard rumors of a youth who bore his name, and who lectured in a temple at Jerusalem to a group of learned doctors. A few years ago we heard that this same youth, grown older, had organized a band of men, that with them he was journeying from place to place, preaching and teaching and aiding the needy. And—" here the boy's father had a habit of lowering his voice and glancing furtively around the room—"there are some who say that he has become a Messiah, and that he does more than champion the cause of the common people. There are some who say that he performs wonderful deeds, healing the halt and the blind and the lepers—even raising the dead."

Once, at this point, the boy interrupted. "I would that I might meet him," he had said with ill-masked eagerness. "I would that he might take the hump from my back and make me strong and straight like other children."

It was growing cold on the hillside. The child drew the shawl closer about his tired body and wished that he were not a shepherd.

Shepherds led a lonely life—they did not fit into the bright places of the world. Rooms gaily lighted at eventide were for the men and boys who worked hard by day and earned their moments of ease; they were not for shepherds. But what else could a crippled lad do to justify his existence—what else than tend sheep? A crippled lad who could not undertake physical labor and who had no talents.

Yawning wearily, the boy glanced at the sky. From the position of the moon he judged it to be middle night—it was still a long while before sunrise; still hours before someone would come to take his place and he could limp home. And yet middle night had its compensations! For at that time he could break his fast and partake of the lunch that his mother had packed so neatly into a basket.

As he reached for the basket, as he opened it slowly, the boy was wondering what had been prepared for his refreshment. He found, to his satisfaction, that there was a flask of goat's milk, and nearly a loaf of crusty dark bread, and some yellow cheese; that there were dried figs, sugary with their own sweetness. And, wrapped separately, he came upon a real treat. A cake made of eggs and sifted flour, with citron in it, and raisins!

He had expected the bread and the cheese and the milk. Even the figs he had expected. But the cake was a surprise, the sort of surprise that happened seldom. His eyes gleamed as he surveyed it, and some of the sadness went out of them. Carefully he set the basket down and spread on the ground beside him the square of linen in which his mother had folded the lunch. Carefully he laid out the flask of milk, the bread, the cheese—but not the cake, which he left tucked away in the depths of the basket. He left it there so that he might not be tempted to eat it first!

"It is good to be hungry," he said aloud. "Yes—and to have food!"

From somewhere just behind him a voice spoke. It was not a loud voice, and yet the music of it seemed to carry beyond the hillside.

"Indeed, yes!" said the voice. "It is good to be hungry. And to have food, and to——"

Startled, for he had thought he was quite alone with his thoughts and the drowsing sheep, the boy glanced back across his crooked shoulder. He saw a man standing upon the brow of the hill, silhouetted against the night sky. Ordinarily he would have known fear, for there were cruel robbers abroad often at middle night. But somehow the sight of this man, who was tall and muscular, failed to frighten him. He did not know why he instinctively completed the man's unfinished sentence.

"And to share it!" he murmured, as if in a dream. "You are a stranger, sir?"

The man came closer to the child and stood looking down upon him. "No, not a stranger," he said slowly, "never a stranger. As it happens, my journey started not far from this very place— started years before you, my lad, saw the light. I am by way of completing a circle."

Although he couldn't imagine what the man meant, the boy made swift response.

"I was about to eat my lunch," he said, indicating the square of linen on which he had arranged the contents of his basket. "One grows ravenous on the hillside. I am a shepherd, sir. I tend my father's flock, and each night my mother packs for me a simple repast. Will you be seated—you who have journeyed so long— and break bread with me? Perhaps—" he hesitated shyly—"you will talk with me as we eat? It grows lonely on the dark hillside— I pine at times for companionship."

The man continued to peer down from his impressive height. His eyes held a warm glow—it was as if a candle burned some- where behind them, the boy thought, and remembered words that his father had spoken when he described a woman in a stable. He felt so comforted by the man's glance that he smiled up into the kindly face, and the man spoke again.

"It is a strange coincidence," he said, "the fact that you are a shepherd, for I also tend my father's flock! And I also—" his smile was luminous—"have often grown lonely waiting for the gates of dawn to open. Are you sure—" he seated himself upon the ground—"that you have enough for two? I should not like to deprive you of anything."

Gazing, fascinated, into the man's face, the boy replied:

"But, yes! I have a large flask of goat's milk, and some yellow cheese, and nearly a loaf of bread, and ten figs. And—" for a second he hesitated—"that's a great plenty," he finished lamely. He did not mention the cake, still wrapped in the basket. For a cake —a cake made of sifted flour and eggs and citron and raisins—was a rare delicacy. And it was not a very big cake.

The man bent forward to retie the thong of a sandal. The boy saw that the sandal was covered with dust. He tried to keep his eyes from glancing toward his lunch basket as he tore the crusty dark bread into fragments.

"Perhaps your feet are aching," he ventured as he placed the fragments in the center of the linen cloth. "This hill is hard to climb. I am close to being spent when I reach the summit of it, but I must needs sit high so that I can watch all the sheep."

The man said slowly: "I have climbed steeper hills than this one, my lad, and know that there are steeper hills to be. My feet do not ache. How long—" abruptly he changed the subject— "have you been crippled?"

Had it come from an ordinary person, the boy would have resented such a display of curiosity. From this man the question seemed a natural one, to be answered naturally.

"Why," he said, "I have never been without a hump between my shoulders. I hate it, but—" he was quoting his mother—"what must be, must be! Still—" his childish face was a trifle unchild-ish—"it is hard to go through life looking like one of the camels that the Wise Men rode when they came from the east——"

The man interrupted. "What, lad," he queried, "do you know of the Wise Men from the east? How does it happen that you should mention them to me on this night? It is—" he bit into a piece of the crusty dark bread—"very curious!"

Laughing softly, the little boy answered. "I suppose the Wise Men are in my mind," he said, "because this is the time of anniversary, and I have been thinking of the baby that was born in a stable. I was hoping—before you arrived—that once again the great star might shine and that the angels might sing. I have, in fact, been watching the sky rather than the sheep."

The man asked another swift question. "What," he queried, "do you know about these holy things—about the star and the song? You are so very young!"

The boy explained. "All Bethlehem," he said, "heard about the star, and about the infant who lay in the manger because there was no room at the inn. I know, perhaps, more than the others, for my father—a child then himself—was one of the shepherds who saw the light from the heavens and heard the angel music . . . Will you—" the boy had taken the flask of goat's milk into his hands—"will you share with me this cup, sir? For perhaps you thirst?"

The man took the flask from the fragile hands. His fingers were powerful and sinewy, but as gentle as a woman's. He said,

"I will share the cup with you, my lad, for I do thirst."

As he watched the man drinking deeply, the boy thought, "It must be tiring to tramp from place to place."

He said on impulse, as the stranger set down the flask, "Will you tell me, sir, of some of the towns in which you have stayed?"

The man answered: "One town is very like another, my lad, with poverty and pain rubbing elbows against wealth, with greed taking toll, all too often, of humanity. With health on one side and illness on the other. With so few gracious deeds that one can do to help the sore distressed—" he turned his face away—"and a lifetime in which to do them so desperately short!"

In a low tone the boy said: "Sometimes, when I was a tot, I hoped that my life might be short, but already I am ten years old. How old, sir, are you? I feel older than my years . . ."

The man's voice was muted as he replied, "I am more than three times your age, lad, but I, too, feel older than my years."

"You shouldn't, because you're so strong," the boy exclaimed. "When is your time of birth, sir? I was born when it was spring."

The man smiled his beautiful, luminous smile. "It's odd that you should ask, dear lad," he murmured, "for this is my day of birth. You, quite unknowing, are giving me an anniversary feast —and never has a feast been more welcome. I was weary and forlorn when I came upon you."

Weary and forlorn! As he stared at the man, the little boy queried:

"Haven't you any people of your own? People with whom you can make merry on your day of birth? When my birthday arrives, Mother prepares a *real* feast for me, and gives me gifts. This shawl I wear she wove for my last birthday. The year before she pressed a sheaf of bright flowers into wax. Once, when I was smaller, she made wondrous sweetmeats of honey and grain."

The man reached over and rested his hand on the little boy's knee. "I fear," he said, "that I have grown too old and large for birthday gifts. Furthermore, my loved ones are not near enough just now to make merry with me. But maybe, who knows, there will be a gift for me at my journey's end."

The boy's knee felt all atingle under the pressure of the friendly hand. He asked, "When, sir, will you come to your journey's end?"

The man did not meet the child's gaze. He replied, "Perhaps very soon!"

The boy was worried. He said: "You don't look happy about it. Don't you want to come to the end of your travels? Don't you want to reach home and see what gift they have in store for you?"

The man hesitated ever so slightly. "Yes," he said at last, "I want to reach—home. But the gift—it may be too beautiful to bear. Or too heavy for me to carry. I suppose—" his face looked drawn in the white moonlight—"I should be getting on. You have made this birthday very sweet, my lad!"

Peeping down at the white cloth with its remnants of bread and cheese, the boy thought: "There seems to be as much food as ever! He couldn't have liked it." Suddenly he was swept by a burning sense of shame. He spoke impetuously, one word tumbling over the other.

"You did not enjoy your food," he said, "and you have had no true birthday feast. That—though you have no way of guessing —is because I have been selfish and mean! I," he gulped out his confession, "have a cake in my basket—a cake that I was saving to eat alone after you left me. It is a cake of sifted flour and eggs and citron and raisins, *and I love cake*. But now," the boy's voice quavered, "I would not enjoy it if I ate it in a solitary fashion; it would choke me! Sir, I desire to give the cake to you as my gift. Perhaps you will munch it later, when the chill of early morn has set in and you are on the road."

The man did not speak, but his eyes were like stars—instead of candles—as he watched his small host lift the cake from the basket and display its rich goodness. It was only when the boy extended it toward him that he broke into speech.

"Ah, my lad," he said, "you have sustained me with your bread, and we have drunk deep of the same cup. So now we will share this cake, which shall be, through your bounty, my birthday cake. We will apportion it evenly and deftly, and we will eat of it together—you and I. And then you shall wait for the dawn, and I will be on my way. But as I walk along the road I shall see a little lad's face, and shall hear a little lad's voice, and shall re-member a little lad's generosity."

Gravely—as if he were handling something infinitely precious —the man took the rich cake into his fingers. Carefully he divided it so that the two sections were equal. He said, "Bless unto us this food, my Father," and the boy was startled, because there was no one else upon the hillside. Then he said,

"This is the cake of life, lad. Enjoy it to the last crumb!"

So he and the boy ate the cake together, and the boy thought that he had never tasted such fare. It was as if the cake's richness were verily the richness of life! As he licked the last crumbs from his fingers he felt that he was gathering force and vigor and purpose. In his mind's eye, for no reason at all, he saw a picture of himself—robust and handsome and brave—striding down the road with his weakness cast from him and his chin high.

"It's like a vision!" he said, but when the man queried, "What do you mean, lad?" he hung his head and was unable to answer.

Indeed, he was silent so long that the man's hand came to rest lightly upon his shoulder—lightly, but, oh, so firmly! There was something in the touch that made tears hang on the boy's lashes, that wrung from him quick words.

"Oh," he cried, "do not leave me, sir! We could be such friends, you and I. Come with me to my home and dwell with my family. My mother will bake many cakes for you, and my father will share with you of his plenty. And I—you may have my bed, and my waxed flowers, and even this fringed shawl that I wear. Do not journey on, sir! Stay with me, here in Bethlehem."

The man spoke. His voice was like a great bell tolling over hill and valley. "I must go on," he said. "I must be about my father's business—I must travel toward my destiny. But I shall never leave you, my lad, for all that. Lo, I am with you always —even unto the end of the world!"

Bowing his head in his hands, covering his misted eyes, the boy was aware of the man's firm fingers traveling up from his shoulder until they touched his hair. But now he couldn't speak, for a pulse drummed in his throat, and a strange rhythm was hammering in his ears. When he raised his head, finally, the man was gone, and the hillside was empty—save for the shadows that were the sheep.

The boy sobbed once, and sharply, with a sense of loss. He struggled to his feet. Only he didn't have to struggle, really, for there was a curious lightness about his body, and a feeling of freshness and peace—a peace that transcended the pain of parting. But it was not until he drew the fringed lamb's-wool shawl tighter across his back that he realized how straight he was standing— *and how straight he would always stand.*

BY MARGARET E. SANGSTER

THE WORKER IN SANDALWOOD

I like to think of this as a true story, but you who read may please yourselves, siding either with the curé, who says Hyacinthe dreamed it all, and did the carving himself in his sleep, or with Madame. I am sure that Hyacinthe thinks it is true, and so does Madame, but then she has the cabinet, with the little birds and the lilies carved at the corners. Monsieur le curé shrugs his patient shoulders; but then he is tainted with the infidelities of cities, good man, having been three times to Montreal, and once in an electric car to Sainte Anne. He and Madame still talk it over whenever they meet, though it happened so many years ago, and each leaves the other forever unconvinced. Meanwhile the dust gathers in the infinite fine lines of the little birds' feathers, and softens the lily stamens where Madame's duster may not go; and the wood, aging, takes on a golden gleam as of immemorial sunsets: pale red wood, heavy with the scent of the ancient East, the wood that Hyacinthe loved.

It was the only wood of that kind which had ever been seen in Terminaison. Pierre L'Oreillard brought it into the workshop one morning, a small heavy bundle wrapped in sacking, and then in burlap, and then in fine soft cloths. He laid it on a pile of shavings, and unwrapped it carefully; and a dim sweetness filled the dark shed and hung heavily in the thin winter sunbeams.

Pierre L'Oreillard rubbed the wood respectfully with his knobby fingers. "It is sandalwood," he explained to Hyacinthe, pride of knowledge making him expansive, "a most precious wood that grows in warm countries, thou great goblin. Smell it, *imbécile.*

It is sweeter than cedar. It is to make a cabinet for the old Madame at the big house. Thy great hands shall smooth the wood, *nigaud,* and I, I, Pierre the cabinet-maker, shall render it beautiful." Then he went out locking the door behind him.

When he was gone Hyacinthe laid down his plane, blew on his stiff fingers, and shambled slowly over to the wood. He was a great clumsy boy of fourteen, dark-faced, very slow of speech, dull-eyed, and uncared for. He was clumsy because it is impossible to move gracefully when you are growing very big and fast on quite insufficient food; he was dull-eyed because all eyes met his unloving; uncared for, because none knew the beauty of his soul. But his heavy young hands could carve simple things like flowers and birds and beasts, to perfection, as the curé pointed out. Simon has a tobacco jar, carved with pine cones and squirrels, and the curé has a pipe whose bowl is the bloom of a moccasin flower, that I have seen. But it is all very long ago. And facts, in those lonely villages, easily become transfigured, touched upon their gray with a golden gleam.

"Thy hands shall smooth the wood, *nigaud,* and I shall render it beautiful," said Pierre L'Oreillard, and went off to drink brandy at the Cinq Châteaux.

Hyacinthe knew that the making of the cabinet would fall to him, as most of the other work did. He also touched the strange sweet wood, and at last laid his cheek against it, while the fragrance caught his breath. "How it is beautiful!" said Hyacinthe, and for the moment his eyes glowed and he was happy. Then the light passed, and with his bent head he shuffled back to his bench through a foam of white shavings curling almost to his knees.

"Madame will want the cabinet next week, for that is Christmas," said Hyacinthe, and fell to work harder than ever, though it was so cold in the shed that his breath hung like a little silver cloud and the steel stung his hands. There was a tiny window to his right, through which, when it was clear of frost, one looked on Terminaison; and that was cheerful and made one whistle. But to the left, through the chink of the ill-fitting door, there was nothing but the forest, and the road dying away in it, and the trees moving heavily under the snow. Yet from there came all of Hyacinthe's dumb dreams and slow reluctant fancies, which he sometimes found able to tell—in wood, not in words.

Brandy was good at the Cinq Châteaux, and Pierre L'Oreillard gave Hyacinthe plenty of directions, but no further help with the cabinet.

"That is to be finished for Madame on the festival, *gros escargot,*" said he, cuffing Hyacinthe's ears furiously; "finished, and with a prettiness about the corners, hearest thou, *ourson?* I suffer from a delicacy of the constitution and a little feebleness in the legs on these days, so that I cannot handle the tools. I must leave this work to thee, *gâcheur.* See it is done properly. And stand up and touch a hand to thy cap when I address thee, *orvet,* great slow-worm."

"Yes, Monsieur," said Hyacinthe wearily.

It is hard, when you do all the work, to be cuffed into the bargain; and fourteen is not very old. He went to work on the cabinet with slow, exquisite skill; but on the eve of Noël he was still at work, and the cabinet unfinished, and Pierre's thrashings were cruel. But it was growing into a thing of perfection under his slow hands, and Hyacinthe would not hurry over it.

"Then work on it all night, and show it to me all completed in the morning, or thy bones shall mourn thine idleness," said Pierre with a flicker of his little eyes. And he shut Hyacinthe into the workshop with a smoky lamp, his tools, and the sandalwood cabinet.

It was nothing unusual. The boy had often been left before to finish a piece of work overnight while Pierre went off to his brandies. But this was Christmas Eve and he was very tired. The cold crept into the shed, until even the scent of the sandalwood could not make him dream himself warm, and the roof cracked sullenly in the frost. There came upon Hyacinthe one of those awful, hopeless despairs that children know. It seemed to be a living presence that caught up his soul and crushed it in black hands. "In all the world nothing!" said he, staring at the dull flame; "no place, no heart, no love! O kind God, is there a place, a love for me in another world?"

I cannot endure to think of Hyacinthe, poor lad, shut up despairing in a workshop with his loneliness, his cold, and his hunger, on the eve of Christmas. He was but an overgrown, unhappy child. And for unhappy children no aid, at this season, seems too divine for faith. So Madame says, and she is very old and very wise. Hyacinthe even looked at the chisel in his hand, and thought that by a touch of that he might lose all, all, and be at peace, somewhere not far from God; only it was forbidden. Then came the tears, and great sobs that sickened and deafened him, so that he scarcely heard the gentle rattling of the latch.

At least, I suppose it came then, but it may have been later. The story is all so vague here, so confused with fancies that have spoiled the first simplicity. I think that Hyacinthe must have gone to the door, opening it upon the still woods and the frosty stars. And that the lad who stood outside in the snow must have said, "I see you are working late, comrade. May I come in?" or something like it.

Hyacinthe brushed his ragged sleeve across his eyes, and opened the door wider with a little nod to the other to enter. Those little lonely villages strung along the great river see strange wayfarers adrift inland from the sea. Hyacinthe said to himself that surely here was such a one.

Afterwards he told the curé that for a moment he had been bewildered. Dully blinking into the stranger's eyes, he lost for a flash the first impression of the youth, and received one of some incredible age of sadness. But this also passed, and he knew that the wanderer's eyes were only quiet, very quiet, like the little pools in the wood where the wild doves went to drink. As he turned within the door, smiling at Hyacinthe and shaking some snow from his fur cap, he did not seem more than sixteen or so.

"It is very cold outside," he said; "there is a big oak tree on the edge of the field that has split in the frost and frightened all the little squirrels there. Next year it will make even a better home for them. And see what I found close by!" He opened his fingers, and showed Hyacinthe a little sparrow lying unruffled in the palm.

"*Pauvrette!*" said the dull Hyacinthe. "*Pauvrette! Is it then dead?*" He touched it with a gentle forefinger.

"No," answered the strange boy, "it is not dead. We will put it here among the shavings, not far from the lamp, and it will be well by morning."

He smiled at Hyacinthe again, and the shambling lad felt dimly as if the scent of the sandalwood had deepened, and the lamp flame burned clearer. But the stranger's eyes were only quiet, quiet.

"Have you come far?" asked Hyacinthe. "It is a bad season for traveling, and the wolves are out in the woods."

"A long way," said the other; "a long, long way. I heard a child cry——"

"There is no child here," answered Hyacinthe, shaking his head. "Monsieur L'Oreillard is not fond of children, he says they cost too much money. But if you have come far, you must be cold and hungry, and I have no food nor fire. At the Cinq Châteaux you will find both."

The stranger looked at him again with those quiet eyes, and Hyacinthe fancied his face was familiar.

"I will stay here," he said. "You are very late at work and you are unhappy."

"Why, as to that," answered Hyacinthe, rubbing again at his cheeks and ashamed of his tears, "most of us are sad at one time or another, the good God knows. Stay here and welcome if it pleases you; and you may take a share of my bed, though it is no more than a pile of balsam boughs and an old blanket in the loft. But I must work at this cabinet, for the drawer must be finished and the handles put on and these corners carved, all by the holy morning; or my wages will be paid with a stick."

"You have a hard master," put in the other boy, "if he would pay you with blows upon the feast of Noël."

"He is hard enough," said Hyacinthe; "but once he gave me a dinner of sausages and white wine, and once, in the summer, melons. If my eyes will stay open, I will finish this by morning, but indeed I am sleepy. Stay with me an hour or so, comrade, and talk to me of your wanderings, so that the time may pass more quickly."

"I will tell you of a country where I was a child," answered the stranger.

And while Hyacinthe worked, he told—of sunshine and dust, of the shadow of vineleaves on the flat white walls of a house; of rosy doves on the flat roof; of the flowers that come out in the spring, crimson and blue, and the white cyclamen in the shadow of the rocks; of the olive, the myrtle and the almond; until Hyacinthe's slow fingers ceased working, and his sleepy eyes blinked wonderingly.

"See what you have done, comrade," he said at last; "you have told of such pretty things that I have done no work for an hour. And now the cabinet will never be finished, and I shall be beaten."

"Let me help you," smiled the other; "I also was born a carpenter."

At first Hyacinthe would not, fearing to trust the sweet wood out of his own hands. But at length he allowed the stranger to fit in one of the little drawers. And so deftly was the work done that Hyacinthe pounded his fists on the bench in admiration. "You have a pretty knack," he cried; "it seemed that you did but hold the drawer in your hands a moment, and hey! ho! it jumped into its place!"

"Let me lift in the other little drawers, while you go and rest awhile," said the wanderer. So Hyacinthe curled up among the shavings, and the stranger fell to work upon the little cabinet of sandalwood.

Here begins what the curé will have it is a dream within a dream. Sweetest of dreams that was ever dreamed, if that is so. Sometimes I am forced to think with him, but again I see as clearly as with old Madame's eyes that have not seen the earthly light for twenty years, and with her and Hyacinthe I say *"Credo."*

Hyacinthe said that he lay among the shavings in the sweetness of the sandalwood, and was very tired. He thought of the country where the stranger had been a boy, of the flowers on the hills, of the laughing leaves of aspen and poplar, of the golden-flowering anise, and the golden sun upon the dusty roads, until he was warm. All the time through these pictures, as through a painted veil, he was aware of that other boy with the quiet eyes, at work upon the cabinet, smoothing, fitting, polishing.

"He does better work than I," thought Hyacinthe; but he was not jealous. And again he thought, "It is growing towards morning. In a little while I will get up and help him." But he did not, for the dream of warmth and the smell of sandalwood held him in a sweet drowse. Also he said he thought the stranger was singing as he worked, for there seemed to be a sense of some music in the shed, though he could not tell whether it came from the other boy's lips, or from the shabby old tools as he used them, or from the stars. "The stars are much paler," thought Hyacinthe, "and soon it will be morning, and the corners are not carved yet. I must get up and help this kind one in a little moment. Only I am so tired, and the sweetness seems to wrap me and fold me close, so that I may not move."

He lay without moving, and behind the forest there shone a pale glow of some indescribable color that was neither green nor blue, while in Terminaison the church bells began to ring.

"Day will soon be here," thought Hyacinthe immovable in that dream of his, "and with day will come Monsieur L'Oreillard and his stick. I must get up and help, for even yet the corners are not carved."

But he did not get up. Instead, he saw the stranger look at him again, smiling as if he loved him, and laying his brown finger lightly upon the four empty corners of the cabinet. And Hyacinthe saw the little squares of reddish wood ripple and heave and break, as little clouds when the wind goes through the sky. And out of them thrust forth the little birds, and after them the lilies, for a moment living, but even while Hyacinthe looked growing hard and reddish-brown and settling back into the sweet wood. Then the stranger smiled again, and laid all the tools neatly in order, and, opening the door quietly, went away into the woods.

Hyacinthe still lay among the shavings for a long time, and then he crept slowly to the door. The sun, not yet risen, sent his first beams upon the delicate mist of frost afloat beneath the trees, and so all the world was aflame with splendid gold. Far away down the road a dim figure seemed to move amid the glory, but the glow and the splendor was such that Hyacinthe was blinded. His breath came sharply as the glow beat in great waves on the wretched shed, and on the foam of shavings, on the cabinet with the little birds and the lilies carved at the corners. He was too pure of heart to feel afraid. But, "Blessed be the Lord," whispered Hyacinthe, clasping his slow hands, "for He hath visited and redeemed his people. But who will believe?"

Then the sun of Christ's day rose gloriously, and the little sparrow came from his nest among the shavings and shook his wings in the light.

BY MARJORIE L. C. PICKTHALL

THE YOUNG
HANS CHRISTIAN ANDERSEN

The big book was returned to its shelf and the father looked down at his son. He smiled at the boy and nodded his head slowly up and down.

The mother sighed. "So he sits with half-shut eyes, dreaming, dreaming, not one word has he heard!"

Hans Christian opened his eyes. "Truly, my mother, every word has gone deep into my heart. I but closed my eyes that I might see more clearly—see that small town of Bethlehem on a night of stars and cold."

The boy rose from his stool and walked over to the window. It was white with frost but he took two warm pennies from the stove and holding them up to the window made peepholes through which he might look. A group of children were going down the street singing, carrying brooms with lanterns fixed to them. The music of their voices came to the boy.

"Was it such a night as this, that first Christmas?" he asked, turning to his father, then turning back again he peered out into the little street that lay under its mantle of softly falling snow.

"The white bees swarm not in Judea," the father spoke slowly, "but it was cold, and sheep lay huddled on the hills closer than the trees in our dark forests. And it was still. There was no sound until the angels came."

"I wish I might hear an angel!" Hans Christian exclaimed.

"So you do, when your heart is filled with peace and there is born in you a great longing to serve the world."

"Tst! Tst!" the mother cried. "What folly you teach the boy! What ideas you put in his head!"

The father smiled and crossed the room to his shoemaker's bench. "Ah, well, Ane Marie, Christmas Eve or no, here is a pair of shoes that I must finish before tomorrow; and you, Hans Christian, must fetch the evening's milk for your mother."

The boy nodded and took down his coat from its peg and pulled on his shoes. Then he picked up a little pail that stood by the stove and, kissing his mother good-bye, went off silently into the night.

Ane Marie watched him trudging through the snow with his gray coat that was too small for him and his wooden shoes that were too big. "If I but knew—" she said to herself, her eyes on the long thin boy with his mop of yellow hair that the night wind was tossing, then she turned to the father. "Hans, Hans, what is to become of this gaunt duckling of ours?"

The father tapped away for a moment without answering.

"He says he will be someone important in the theater, or even a poet," the mother went on, "and he so awkward and ungainly with that great nose of his and those small eyes!"

"Should he not know more of his own life than others?" the father asked quietly.

"The townsfolk call him vain and make fun of him," the mother went on as if she had not heard, "and were it not for his long legs for running and his long arms for climbing his face would have known Odense cobbles long before this."

The father nodded. "Ofttimes the world treats hardest those who serve her best. I know these things are sad, Ane Marie, but trouble not yourself. To the boy, the knowledge of his future is more real than the taunts of his playfellows. I know not what he will become, but mind—force him to nothing. Let him have his own way. Those dreams that others scorn may be his wings."

Hans Christian walked slowly through the streets of Odense. The snow had ceased falling and in the sky a few stars had appeared. There were candles twinkling in the houses and a distant glimmer over the snow told of the quick play of northern lights.

The boy was glad and grateful for the comfort of light about him. For all his ten years and big body he had a secret terror of the dark. Stories of witches and goblins that his mother often told troubled him.

The boy shivered with remembering. Listening to his father's reading he had quite forgot to put a bowl of gruel in the rafters for the gnomes that were abroad tonight. What would they do to him if they were angered? A sleigh came jingling down the street and the boy drew aside to let it pass. Even now people were returning from church for their trees and their Christmas dinners.

Near the end of the town stood a large house. Candles shone in its windows. No blinds were drawn. Hans Christian, attracted by the light and longing within him for all it meant, approached the house. Standing deep in the snow he gazed into a room where a great fir tree had been brought from the forest. Wax tapers, red, blue and white, were alight on its green branches, while sugar plums and apples, dolls and toys hung from them. On the topmost branch a tinsel star gleamed in the light that burned higher and higher from the tapers.

"Take a white pin in your mouth and you will be invisible," the boy whispered the old saying to himself, well knowing that if anyone should catch sight of him there would be but taunts and mockery for the son of the poor washerwoman.

Hans Christian trembled, not with the cold but with joy at the beauty before him. Then the room began to fill with children reaching eagerly for their presents. Alone in the dark, the boy reached out his arms to the tree, wondering what it was thinking of, what it was feeling. He forgot that the wind was cold, the night dark. He thought no longer of his shabby clothes. Delighting in the tree, he would enquire its secret thoughts.

Then he remembered the milk and hurried on his way. The lighted houses were behind him and the path led along the dark edge of the forest. Fear gripped the boy.

"If I can only remember," he said to himself, seeking courage where he might find it, "that this is the field where, in the summer, I gather wild strawberries and string them on blades of grass; that here I made wreaths for mother; that now I am crossing the stream where I have made boats of rushes and set them sailing—if I can only remember, then these things are still my friends and the edge of the forest is a pleasant place even though it is very dark."

Walking with half-shut eyes and talking assuringly to himself, he reached the farmhouse. The flow of light and warmth that enveloped him when the door was opened cheered him as much as did the bowl of rice gruel and the sweet Christmas cake which the good wife pressed upon him.

"We poor folk have no gifts to give each other," she said to the boy, "but we can share what we have."

Suddenly the boy shouted aloud. "Look! Look! I have the almond in my gruel."

"That is for your good fortune."

Hans Christian smiled. The gnomes could not harm him now, no matter how vexed they were with him, for he had found the almond in his gruel.

"Now, I have a gift for you," he said eagerly, "and I can give it to you as well as keep it myself to give to others. God gave it to me, is not that beautiful?"

Lifting his head he sang in a high clear voice a song of Christmas—a song of sheep and a helpless babe and light that dispelled all darkness.

"I thought the birds sang not in winter," the good wife murmured.

The old farmer nodded in his corner. "Truly, there are seeds in that young heart which need but the sun to burst into flower."

Hans Christian smiled. "Had you not liked my song I would have been sad, now I am happy."

"How came you to know that song?" the farmer asked.

"It is the story my father read to me before I came out this

[225]

evening," the boy answered, smiling brightly at them.

"Some alchemy within the lad turns whatever he hears to song," the good wife said softly.

The old farmer nodded. "It is the singers of the world and the story tellers who carry light."

The boy looked puzzled, then he shook his head quickly. "Ah, but I shall not be one of them. I shall be a dancer, or an actor perhaps. People will clap their hands for me and throw flowers at my feet."

The old man looked at him. "You shall be what God wills."

Hans Christian thought for a moment then, reaching down for his little pail and smiling to the two, he bade good evening and went out into the night.

After the light within the night seemed intensely dark and Hans Christian could not see his way. "Dear God," he spoke aloud, "I have but one hand to give you as I must carry the milk with the other, but let me put that hand in yours."

Slowly he retraced the path. The night became clearer and where fear had been in his heart there was now only a great reverence for the earth that was so thick with snow, the sky that was so dazzling with stars, and the forest that was so sweet with the fragrance of its thousand firs.

He thought of the Christmas tree that he had seen, then of his own humble home and of the story his father had read him from the Bible, while such a glow of thankfulness surged within him that he felt warmed all over.

True, he had no tree, but the trees of the forest were his, and instead of a single star on a topmost branch they were hung with countless stars glimmering diamond-like in the night. While beyond in the distance, but only when he closed his eyes, he could see another tree and on it hung thin books bound in bright colors; but the words on the books he could not see.

In the books there were stories for the little ones of the world —stories of flowers, of mice and snails and small creatures, of toys, of an oak tree, of the sunshine and the dew. Everything that lived, from a fir to a daisy, even inanimate things like lamp posts and houses, told their own stories, had their own feelings. The language of the birds and the winds was told in the books, and the voice of the past could be heard speaking through tales and legends. Each story, though it seemed a simple tale, held within itself some deeply distilled essence, as the violet who first delights with her beauty reveals a deeper secret to those who bend close to her heart.

"It is the story tellers of the world who carry light," Hans Christian murmured, remembering the old man's words.

Somewhere the wind was saying that to the heart of a child dew, rain, sparrows and God's other messengers would always speak on in simplicity and beauty.

Hans Christian was trembling. Who was there to write these tales? Who would give to these things characters of their own, so wrapping them in a mantle of understanding? Not he, for he was to be a great actor. Even when he distrusted himself most, he knew this best. But did the Christ child know what gift of the Wisemen's three would be most precious to him? Gold might have held his baby eyes but myrrh was one day to unlock the treasures of his heart.

The air in the forest was like music and the glow of starlight on the snow came into the boy's heart with the warmth and force of a sunbeam. In that glow he knew that he could climb like a flower out of poverty and ignorance into joy and usefulness. The gifts on the trees in the starlit forest were from God. God. saw him now and knew, better than Hans Christian ever could, what gift was best. Not music filled the air but angels as the boy felt the brushing of their wings.

Hans Christian dropped on his knees in the snow. On this night of giving he would thank God who gave thoughts to men, "Oh, may I never do one deed or write one word of which I shall not be able to account to Thee, dear God."

Suddenly, remembering the milk, the boy rose quickly from the snow and hurried along the path back to the town. As he passed the house where the tree had glittered, he stopped for a moment to look in the windows. There it stood, but its branches were stripped of presents and only guttered tapers remained where light had gleamed. Hans Christian looked up to the heavens where the stars shone steadfastly. "God's candles never go out," he cried fervently, then ran home, his lips forming the praise his heart prompted.

His father was still tapping away at his bench on the pair of shoes. His mother was busy in the little kitchen with its shining pots and pans and clean white curtains. Hans Christian slipped in quietly with the milk and left it with his mother. The father looked up and smiled. The boy said nothing. Sitting down on the floor, Hans Christian drew from under the bed the little theater that his father had made for him. He took the dolls and stood them in rows and then, threading a needle with queer deftness, began to cut out small bits of cloth and sew them together as costumes for his actors.

Ane Marie, coming in from the kitchen, saw the boy absorbed in his work. She nodded to the father. "It is seeing him do that," she said quietly, "that makes me feel he should be apprenticed to a tailor."

BY ELIZABETH YATES

Far down in the forest, where the warm sun and the fresh air made a sweet resting place, grew a pretty little fir tree. And yet it was not so happy—it wished so much to be tall like its companions, the pines and firs which grew around it. The sun shone, the soft air fluttered its leaves, and the little peasant children passed by, prattling merrily, but the fir tree heeded them not. Sometimes the children would bring a large basket of raspberries or strawberries, wreathed on a straw, and seat themselves near the fir tree and say, "Is this not a pretty little tree?" which made it feel more unhappy than before.

And yet all this while the tree grew a notch or joint taller every year—for by the number of joints in the stem of a fir tree we can discover its age. Still, as it grew it complained, "Oh, how I wish I were as tall as the other trees. Then I would spread out my branches on every side, and my top would overlook the wide world. I should have the birds building their nests on my boughs, and when the wind blew, I should bow with stately dignity like my tall companions."

The tree was so discontented that it took no pleasure in the warm sunshine, the birds, or the rosy clouds that floated over it morning and evening. Sometimes in winter, when the snow lay white and glittering on the ground, a hare would come springing along and would jump right over the little tree, and then how mortified it would feel!

Two winters passed; and when the third arrived, the tree had grown so tall that the hare was obliged to run round it. Yet it remained dissatisfied and would exclaim, "Oh, if I could but keep on growing tall and old! There is nothing else worth caring for in the world."

In the autumn, as usual, the woodcutters came and cut down several of the tallest trees. And the young fir tree, which was not grown to its full height, shuddered as the noble trees fell to the earth with a crash. After the branches were lopped off, the trunks looked so slender and bare that they could scarcely be recognized. Then they were placed upon wagons and drawn by horses out of the forest. "Where were they going? What would become of them?" The young fir tree wished very much to know. So in the spring, when the swallows and the storks came, it asked, "Do you know where those trees were taken? Did you meet them?"

The swallows knew nothing, but the stork, after a little reflection, nodded his head and said, "Yes, I think I do. I met several new ships when I flew from Egypt, and they had masts that smelt like fir. I think these must have been the trees. I assure you they were stately, very stately."

"Oh, how I wish I were tall enough to go on the sea," said the fir tree. "What is this sea, and what is it like?"

"It would take too much time to explain," said the stork, flying quickly away.

"Rejoice in thy youth," said the sunbeam. "Rejoice in thy fresh growth and the young life that is in thee." And the wind kissed the tree and the dew watered it with tears, but the fir tree regarded them not.

Christmas drew near and many young trees were cut down, some even smaller and younger than the fir tree, who enjoyed neither rest nor peace from longing to leave its forest home. These young trees, chosen for their beauty, kept their branches, but they too were laid on wagons and drawn by horses out of the forest.

"Where are they going?" asked the fir tree. "They are no taller than I am. Indeed, one is much shorter. And why are the branches not cut off? Where are they going?"

"We know. We know," sang the sparrows. "We have looked in at the windows of the houses in town, and we know what is done with them. They are dressed up in the most splendid manner. We have seen them standing in the middle of a warm room, and adorned with all sorts of beautiful things—honey cakes, gilded apples, playthings, and many hundreds of wax tapers."

"And then," asked the fir tree, trembling through all its branches, "and then what happens?"

"We did not see any more," said the sparrows. "But that was enough for us."

"I wonder whether anything so brilliant will ever happen to me," thought the fir tree. "It would be much better than crossing the sea. I long for it almost with pain. Oh, when will Christmas be here? I am now as tall and well grown as those which were taken away last year. Oh, that I were now laid on the wagon, or standing in the warm room, with all that brightness and splendor around me! Something better and more beautiful is to come after, or the trees would not be so decked out. Yes, what follows will be grander and more splendid. What can it be? I am weary with longing. I scarcely know how I feel."

"Rejoice with us," said the air and the sunlight. "Enjoy thine own bright life in the fresh air."

But the tree would not rejoice, though it grew taller every day. And winter and summer its dark green foliage might be seen in the forest, while passers-by would say, "What a beautiful tree!"

A short time before Christmas, the discontented fir tree was the first to fall. As the ax cut through the stem and divided the pith, the tree fell with a groan to the earth, conscious of pain and faintness, and forgetting all its anticipations of happiness in sorrow at leaving its home in the forest. It knew that it should never again see its dear old companions, the trees, nor the little bushes and many-colored flowers that had grown by its side; perhaps not even the birds. Neither was the journey at all pleasant. The tree first recovered itself while being unpacked with several other trees in the courtyard of a house, and it heard a man say, "We want only one, and this is the prettiest."

Then came two servants in grand livery and carried the fir tree into a large and beautiful apartment. On the walls hung pictures and near the great stove stood great china vases, with lions on the lids. There were rocking chairs, silken sofas, and large tables covered with pictures, books, and playthings worth a great deal of money. At least, the children said so. Then the fir tree was placed in a large tub full of sand, but green baize hung all around it so that no one could see it was a tub, and it stood on a very handsome carpet. How the fir tree trembled! "What is going to happen to me now?" Some young ladies came and the servants helped them to adorn the tree. On one branch they hung little bags cut out of colored paper, and each bag was filled with sweetmeats. From other branches hung gilded apples and walnuts as if they had grown there. And above and all around were hundreds of red, blue, and white tapers, which were fastened on the branches. Dolls exactly like real babies were placed under the green leaves—the tree had never seen such things before! And at the very top was fastened a glittering star made of tinsel. Oh, it was very beautiful!

"This evening," they all exclaimed, "how bright it will be!" "Oh, that the evening were here!" thought the tree. "And the tapers lighted! Then I shall know what else is going to happen. Will the trees of the forest come to see me? I wonder if the sparrows will peep in at the windows as they fly? Shall I grow faster here, and keep on all these ornaments during summer and winter?" But guessing was of very little use. It made his bark ache, and this pain is as bad for a slender fir tree as a headache is for us. At last the tapers were lighted and then what a glistening blaze of light the tree presented! It trembled so with joy in all its branches that one of the candles fell among the green leaves and burnt some of them. "Help! Help!" exclaimed the young ladies, but there was no danger, for they quickly extinguished the fire. After this the tree tried not to tremble at all, though the fire frightened him. He was so anxious not to hurt any of the beautiful ornaments, even while their brilliancy dazzled him. And now the folding doors were thrown open and a troop of children rushed in as if they intended to upset the tree. They were followed more slowly by their elders. For a moment the little ones stood silent with astonishment, and then they shouted for joy till the room rang, and they danced merrily round the tree, while one present after another was taken from it.

"What are they doing? What will happen next?" thought the fir. At last the candles burnt down to the branches and were put out. Then the children received permission to plunder the tree.

Oh, how they rushed upon it, till the branches cracked, and had it not been fastened with the glistening star to the ceiling, it must have been thrown down. The children then danced about with their pretty toys, and no one noticed the tree except the children's maid, who came and peeped among the branches to see if an apple or a fig had been forgotten. "A story! A story!" cried the children, pulling a little fat man towards the tree.

"Now we shall be in the green shade," said the man, as he seated himself under it, "and the tree will have the pleasure of hearing also, but I shall only relate one story. What shall it be? Ivede-Avede? Or Humpty Dumpty, who fell downstairs but soon got up again, and at last married a princess?"

"Ivede-Avede," cried some. "Humpty Dumpty," cried others, and there was a fine shouting and crying out. The fir tree remained quite still and thought to himself, "Shall I have anything to do with all this?" But he had already amused them as much as they wished. Then the old man told them the story of Humpty Dumpty—how he fell downstairs, and was raised up again, and married a princess. And the children clapped their hands and cried, "Tell another! Tell another!" They wanted to hear the story of Ivede-Avede, but they only had Humpty Dumpty. After this the fir tree became quite silent and thoughtful. Never had the birds in the forest told such tales as Humpty Dumpty, who fell downstairs and yet married a princess.

"Ah, yes, so it happens in the world," thought the fir tree. He believed it all, because it was related by such a nice man. "Ah, well," he thought, "who knows? Perhaps I may fall down too, and marry a princess." And he looked forward joyfully to the next evening, expecting to be again decked out with lights and playthings, gold and fruit. "Tomorrow I will not tremble," thought he. "I will enjoy all my splendor, and I shall hear the story of Humpty Dumpty again, and perhaps Ivede-Avede." And the tree remained quiet and thoughtful all night. In the morning the servants and the housemaid came in.

"Now," thought the fir, "all my splendor is going to begin again." But they dragged him out of the room and upstairs to the garret and threw him on the floor, in a dark corner where no daylight shone, and there they left him. "What does this mean?" thought the tree. "What am I to do here? I can hear nothing in a place like this!" And he leaned against the wall and thought and thought.

He had time enough to think, for days and nights passed and no one came near him, and when at last somebody did come, it was only to put away large boxes in a corner. So the tree was completely hidden from sight as if it had never existed. "It is winter now," thought the tree. "The ground is hard and covered with snow, so that people cannot plant me. I shall be sheltered here, I daresay, until spring comes. How thoughtful and kind everybody is to me! Still I wish this place were not so dark as well as lonely, with not even a little hare to look at. How pleasant it was out in the forest when the snow lay on the ground. Then the hare would run by, yes, and jump over me too, although I did not like it then. Oh, it is terribly lonely here!"

"Squeak, squeak," said a little mouse, creeping cautiously towards the tree. Then came another, and they both sniffed at the fir tree and crept between the branches.

"Oh, it is very cold," said the mouse, "or else we should be so comfortable here, shouldn't we, you old fir tree?"

"I am not old," said the fir tree. "There are many who are older than I am."

"Where do you come from and what do you know?" asked the mice, who were full of curiosity. "Have you seen the most beautiful places in the world, and can you tell us all about them? And have you been in the storeroom, where cheeses lie on the shelf and hams hang from the ceiling? One can run about on tallow candles there, and go in thin and come out fat."

"I know nothing of that place," said the fir tree. "But I know the wood where the sun shines and the birds sing." And then the tree told the little mice all about its youth. They had never heard such an account in their lives. After they had listened to it attentively, they said, "What a number of things you have seen! You must have been very happy."

"Happy?" exclaimed the fir tree. And then as he reflected upon what he had been telling them, he said, "Ah, yes. After all, those were happy days." But when he went on and related all about Christmas Eve, and how he had been dressed up with cakes and lights, the mice said, "How happy you must have been, you old fir tree!"

"I am not old at all," replied the tree. "I only came from the forest this winter. I am now checked in my growth."

"What splendid stories you can relate," said the little mice. And the next night four other mice came with them to hear what the tree had to tell. The more he talked, the more he remembered, and then he thought to himself, "Those were happy days, but they may come again. Humpty Dumpty fell downstairs, and yet he married the princess. Perhaps I may marry a princess too." And the fir tree thought of the pretty little birch tree that grew in the forest, which was to him a real beautiful princess.

"Who is Humpty Dumpty?" asked the little mice, and then the tree related the whole story. He could remember every single word, and the little mice were so delighted with it that they were ready to jump to the top of the tree. The next night a great many more mice came, and on Sunday two rats came with them. But the rats said it was not a pretty story at all, and the little mice were very sorry, for it made them also think less of it.

"Do you know only one story?" asked the rats.

"Only one," replied the fir tree. "I heard it on the happiest evening in my life, but I did not know I was so happy at the time."

"We think it is a very miserable story," said the rats. "Don't you know any story about bacon or tallow in the storeroom?"

"No," replied the tree.

"Many thanks to you then," replied the rats, and they marched off.

The little mice also kept away after this, and the tree sighed and said, "It was very pleasant when the merry little mice sat round me and listened while I talked. Now that is all past too. However, I shall consider myself happy when someone comes to take me out of this place." But would this ever happen? Yes, one morning people came to clear out the garret. The boxes were packed away, and the tree was pulled out of the corner and thrown roughly on the garret floor. Then the servant dragged it out upon the staircase where the daylight shone.

"Now life is beginning again," said the tree, rejoicing in the sunshine and fresh air. Then it was carried downstairs and taken into the courtyard so quickly that it forgot to think of itself, and could only look about. There was so much to be seen! The court was close to a garden, where everything looked blooming. Fresh and fragrant roses hung over the little palings. The linden trees were in blossom, while the swallows flew here and there, crying, "Twit, twit, twit, my mate is coming." But it was not the fir tree they meant.

"Now I shall live," cried the tree, joyfully spreading out its branches. But alas, they were all withered and yellow, and it lay in a corner amongst weeds and nettles. The star of gold paper still stuck in the top of the tree and glittered in the sunshine.

In the same courtyard were playing two of the merry children who had danced round the tree at Christmas and had been so happy. The youngest saw the gilded star and ran and pulled it off the tree.

"Look what is sticking to the old ugly fir tree," said the child, treading on the branches till they crackled under his boots. And the tree saw all the fresh bright flowers in the garden, and then looked at itself and wished it had remained in the dark corner of the garret. It thought of its fresh youth in the forest, of the merry Christmas evening, and of the little mice who had listened to the story of Humpty Dumpty.

"Past! past!" said the old tree. "Oh, had I but enjoyed myself while I could have done so! Now it is too late."

Then a lad came and chopped the tree into small pieces, till a large bundle lay in a heap on the ground. The pieces were placed in a fire under the kettle, and they quickly blazed up brightly, while the tree sighed so deeply that each sigh was like a little pistol shot. Then the children, who were at play, came and seated themselves in front of the fire, and looked at it and cried, "Pop, pop." But at each "pop," which was a deep sigh, the tree was thinking of a summer day in the forest, or of some winter night there when the stars shone brightly, and of Christmas evening, and of Humpty Dumpty, the only story it had ever heard or knew how to relate—till at last it was consumed.

The boys still played in the garden, and the youngest wore on his breast the golden star with which the tree had been adorned during the happiest evening of its existence. Now all was past: the tree's life was past, and the story also—for all stories must come to an end at last.

BY HANS CHRISTIAN ANDERSEN

If you walk through a grove of balsam trees you will notice that the young trees are silent; they are listening. But the old tall ones—especially the firs—are whispering. They are telling the story of The Tree That Didn't Get Trimmed. It sounds like a painful story, and the murmur of the old trees as they tell it is rather solemn; but it is an encouraging story for young saplings to hear. On warm autumn days when your trunk is tickled by ants and insects climbing, and the resin is hot and gummy in your knots, and the whole glade smells sweet, drowsy, and sad, and the hardwood trees are boasting of the gay colours they are beginning to show, many a young evergreen has been cheered by it.

All young fir trees, as you know by that story of Hans Andersen's—if you've forgotten it, why not read it again?—dream of being a Christmas Tree some day. They dream about it as young girls dream of being a bride, or young poets of having a volume of verse published. With the vision of that brightness and gayety before them they patiently endure the sharp sting of the ax, the long hours pressed together on a freight car. But every December there are more trees cut down than are needed for Christmas. And that is the story that no one—not even Hans Andersen— has thought to put down.

The tree in this story should never have been cut. He wouldn't have been, but it was getting dark in the Vermont woods, and the man with the ax said to himself, "Just one more . . ."

He was a fine, well-grown youngster, but too tall for his age; his branches were rather scraggly. If he'd been left there he would have been an unusually big tree some day; but now he was in the awkward age and didn't have the tapering shape and the thick, even foliage that people like on Christmas trees. Worse still, instead of running up to a straight, clean spire, his top was a bit lop-sided, with a fork in it.

But he didn't know this as he stood with many others, leaning against the side wall of the greengrocer's shop. In those cold December days he was very happy, thinking of the pleasures to come. He had heard of the delights of Christmas Eve: the stealthy setting-up of the tree, the tinsel balls and coloured toys and stars, the peppermint canes and birds with spun-glass tails. Even that old anxiety of Christmas trees—burning candles— did not worry him, for he had been told that nowadays people use strings of tiny electric bulbs which cannot set one on fire. So he looked forward to the festival with a confident heart.

"I shall be very grand," he said. "I hope there will be children to admire me. It must be a great moment when the children hang their stockings on you!" He even felt sorry for the first trees that were chosen and taken away. It would be best, he considered, not to be bought until Christmas Eve. Then, in the shining darkness someone would pick him out, put him carefully along the running board of a car, and away they would go. The tire-chains would clack and jingle merrily on the snowy road. He imagined a big house with fire glowing on a hearth; the hushed rustle of wrapping paper and parcels being unpacked. Someone would say, "Oh, what a beautiful tree!" How erect and stiff he would brace himself in his iron tripod stand.

But day after day went by, one by one the other trees were taken, and he began to grow troubled. For everyone who looked at him seemed to have an unkind word. "Too tall," said one lady. "No, this one wouldn't do, the branches are too skimpy," said another. "If I chop off the top," said the greengrocer, "it wouldn't be so bad?" The tree shuddered, but the customer had already passed on to look at others. Some of his branches ached where the grocer had bent them upward to make his shape more attractive.

Across the street was a Ten Cent Store. Its bright windows

were full of scarlet odds and ends; when the doors opened he could see people crowded along the aisles, cheerfully jostling one another with bumpy packages. A buzz of talk, a shuffle of feet, a constant ringing of cash drawers came noisily out of that doorway. He could see flashes of marvellous colour, ornaments for luckier trees. Every evening, as the time drew nearer, the pavements were more thronged. The handsomer trees, not so tall as he but more bushy and shapely, were ranked in front of him; as they were taken away he could see the gayety only too well. Then he was shown to a lady who wanted a tree very cheap. "You can have this one for a dollar," said the grocer. This was only one third of what the grocer had asked for him at first, but even so the lady refused him and went across the street to buy a little artificial tree at the toy store. The man pushed him back carelessly, and he toppled over and fell alongside the wall. No one bothered to pick him up. He was almost glad, for now his pride would be spared.

Now it was Christmas Eve. It was a foggy evening with a drizzling rain; the alley alongside the store was thick with trampled slush. As he lay there among broken boxes and fallen scraps of holly strange thoughts came to him. In the still northern forest already his wounded stump was buried in forgetful snow. He remembered the wintry sparkle of the woods, the big trees with crusts and clumps of silver on their broad boughs, the keen singing of the lonely wind. He remembered the strong, warm feeling of his roots reaching down into the safe earth. That is a good feeling; it means to a tree just what it means to you to stretch your toes down toward the bottom of a well-tucked bed. And he had given up all this to lie here, disdained and forgotten, in a littered alley. The splash of feet, the chime of bells, the cry of cars went past him. He trembled a little with self-pity and vexation. "No toys and stockings for me," he thought sadly, and shed some of his needles.

Late that night, after all the shopping was over, the grocer came out to clear away what was left. The boxes, the broken wreaths, the empty barrels, and our tree with one or two others that hadn't been sold, all were thrown through the side door into the cellar. The door was locked and he lay there in the dark. One of his branches, doubled under him in the fall, ached so he thought it must be broken. "So this is Christmas," he said to himself.

All that day it was very still in the cellar. There was an occasional creak as one of the bruised trees tried to stretch itself. Feet went along the pavement overhead, and there was a booming of church bells, but everything had a slow, disappointed sound. Christmas is always a little sad, after such busy preparations. The unwanted trees lay on the stone floor, watching the furnace light flicker on a hatchet that had been left there.

The day after Christmas a man came in who wanted some green boughs to decorate a cemetery. The grocer took the hatchet, and seized the trees without ceremony. They were too disheartened to care. Chop, chop, chop, went the blade, and the sweet-smelling branches were carried away. The naked trunks were thrown into a corner.

And now our tree, what was left of him, had plenty of time to think. He no longer could feel anything, for trees feel with their branches, but they think with their trunks. What did he think about as he grew dry and stiff? He thought that it had been silly of him to imagine such a fine, gay career for himself, and he was sorry for other young trees, still growing in the fresh hilly country, who were enjoying the same fantastic dreams.

Now perhaps you don't know what happens to the trunks of leftover Christmas trees. You could never guess. Farmers come in from the suburbs and buy them at five cents each for bean-poles and grape arbours. So perhaps (here begins the encouraging part of this story) they are really happier, in the end, than the trees that get trimmed for Santa Claus. They go back into the fresh, moist earth of spring, and when the sun grows hot the quick tendrils of the vines climb up them and presently they are decorated with the red blossoms of the bean or the little blue globes of the grape, just as pretty as any Christmas trinkets.

So one day the naked, dusty fir-poles were taken out of the cellar, and thrown into a truck with many others, and made a rattling journey out into the land. The farmer unloaded them in his yard and was stacking them up by the barn when his wife came out to watch him.

"There!" she said. "That's just what I want, a nice long pole with a fork in it. Jim, put that one over there to hold up the clothesline." It was the first time that anyone had praised our tree, and his dried-up heart swelled with a tingle of forgotten sap. They put him near one end of the clothesline, with his stump close to a flower bed. The fork that had been despised for a Christmas star was just the thing to hold up a clothesline. It was washday, and soon the farmer's wife began bringing out wet garments to swing and freshen in the clean, bright air. And the very first thing that hung near the top of the Christmas pole was a cluster of children's stockings.

That isn't quite the end of the story, as the old fir trees whisper it in the breeze. The Tree That Didn't Get Trimmed was so cheerful watching the stockings, and other gay little clothes that plumped out in the wind just as though waiting to be spanked, that he didn't notice what was going on—or going up—below him. A vine had caught hold of his trunk and was steadily twisting upward. And one morning, when the farmer's wife came out intending to shift him, she stopped and exclaimed. "Why, I mustn't move this pole," she said. "The morning glory has run right up it." So it had, and our bare pole was blue and crimson with colour.

Something nice, the old firs believe, always happens to the trees that don't get trimmed. They even believe that some day one of the Christmas-tree bean-poles will be the starting point for another Magic Beanstalk, as in the fairy tale of the boy who climbed up the bean-tree and killed the giant. When that happens, fairy tales will begin all over again.

BY CHRISTOPHER MORLEY

THE LITTLE GUEST

Every year, at about Christmastime, the holy child came on a visit to the nuns. He came with his mother and Saint Joseph and the shepherds and all the pet animals, and they all stayed together in the little house that the nuns fixed up for them.

The house stood on a table, in the entry just outside the chapel. First there was a white cloth over the table, with lace edges hanging down. On this stood the house. It had only a roof and one wall, at the back, so that you could see right inside it. Behind were the mountains that Sister Gertrude had made, of brown paper covered with sparkly snow, and there were evergreens all round, and ivy, and two real little pine trees growing by themselves in pots.

The holy child seemed to like his little house. He lay just inside it, smiling, on a bed of straw, with a little white shirt on. He didn't seem to mind about its only having one wall, or that the nuns hadn't thought about putting any furniture in it. He lay there and smiled, with his arms stretched out. His mother and Saint Joseph knelt, one on each side, and behind them knelt two angels. That made five people, and the little house wouldn't hold any more, so the shepherds had to stand outside, as close as they could get, and near them stood the animals, the cow and the gray donkey and the three white lambs, two lying down and one standing up. The standing-up one was a little bigger than the others, and had a red collar on. When all the candles were lighted it looked just like a party, with the holy child in the middle.

Twice a day, going to chapel and coming out, the file of little blue-pinafored girls passed the table where the holy child lived; fourteen heads, two by two, brown and yellow and mouse-colored under their thin starched veils, bobbing by sedately, with wrinkled, kindly Sister Elizabeth in her black robes walking behind. Going to and from chapel there was no time to pause, because all the older girls walked behind and one had to keep moving; one had only a glimpse in passing of the little house with all the family gathered round it, bright and dazzling in the light of the wax candles. But every evening at Christmastime, instead of going up the two long straight flights of stairs to the landing outside the dormitory, where the little girls usually said their prayers, Sister Elizabeth would take them the long way round, down the hall and up the back staircase' and through a door by the linen room to the chapel entry.

To Louisa, spending her first Christmas with the nuns, there was something very exciting in this detour. The back stairway was rather dark; the boards creaked underfoot and it had a queer cupboardy smell. There were shadowy corners in it, and the most shadowy place of all was just by the linen-room door. Here you had to stand still and wait, and not make any noise because this was the nun's part of the house and next door to the chapel. You had to stand very quietly while Sister Elizabeth's feet in their flat shoes came creak, creak along the passage, past all the little girls in turn, till she reached the door and turned the handle.

And then, when the door swung open, there were the candles shining, and the Christmasy smell of evergreens and hot melting wax, and in the middle of all this sudden brightness was the little holy child on his straw bed.

Kneeling on the hard boards that always made her shift and wriggle long before Sister Elizabeth's measured voice reached the last "Amen," Louisa had a good view of the little house and everything about it. The mountains looked just like real, the snow glittered on the evergreen branches and on the white cotton batting where the shepherds stood. It was as if you could walk right up between the pine trees, past the gray donkey and the lambs, straight into the little room where the holy child lay. It was all very beautiful.

And yet there was something about it not quite right.

Privately, Louisa had her own opinion of how the nuns treated the holy child.

The snow was lovely, and so were Sister Gertrude's mountains and the little pine trees, but something better could have been done about the house. There was no furniture, there were no curtains; there wasn't even a rug. It was true that the holy child stayed in bed, but he couldn't be very comfortable even there. It was made of straw and it looked prickly, and the holy child had only a small shirt on. There should certainly have been a pillow, and as long as the nuns sewed so well they could have made sheets and a quilt and a little blanket too. Louisa supposed that they just hadn't

thought about it, which was funny, because they had known for days and days that the holy child was coming. It was no way to treat a guest, and the holy child was a guest; Sister Elizabeth had said so.

Nuns, Louisa thought, were very curious people.

It was unusually cold that Christmas. When you went outdoors, even for a moment, your toes pinched and the wind stung your face. Indoors the little girls had to wear their sweaters going to chapel and along the corridors, and when they got up in the morning their fingers were pink and stiff. Because the big register in the floor, for some reason or other, was not giving all the heat it should, Sister Elizabeth brought an oil heater and stood it on the dormitory floor, and the children dressed around that.

There came the frostiest day of all.

Tucked in bed that evening, her toes drawn up under her nightgown to keep them from touching the chilly sheets, Louisa thought about the holy child. He must be terribly cold down there. The nuns, evidently, were doing nothing about it. They didn't even seem worried. They wouldn't mind if the holy child froze!

The oil heater, turned low, glowed like a red eye in the middle of the dormitory floor. Through the looped-up curtains of her bed Louisa could see the long shadows it threw across the floor and up the walls. From the other beds came occasional rustlings and the small breathing sounds of sleep. Louisa tried to sleep too. But every time she shut her eyes she saw the holy child, with only his little shirt on, lying there on the straw bed as she had seen him that evening.

Presently she heard, far off and hollow, the three tolls of the gateway bell, and after what seemed a very long time, the slow, tired steps of Sister Saint Ann, the portress, making her last round. She came along the lower corridor, up the stairway, carrying her lantern, and then Louisa could hear the clink as she set it down finally at the head of the dormitory stairs, where it would burn until morning.

For a little while longer Louisa lay still, the blanket dragged up to her chin. Then very cautiously she pushed back the covers, slid first one leg, then the other, out of bed. It was chilly on the floor. Louisa felt for her slippers, pulled on her dressing gown. Edging her way past the other beds with their humped, sleeping mounds, she reached the doorway and the open landing.

There were two stairways. One, where the lantern stood, was that which the children always used. The other, narrower and steeper, led down through the nuns' part of the house to the chapel entry. Little girls had no business here alone, especially at night.

Holding her breath, Louisa began to creep down, praying that the boards would not creak. The first landing at the bottom was easy; one turned to the right. There was a big room to cross, lined with closets; then came a corridor, another little flight of steps, and then one reached the chapel entry.

There was nothing to be afraid of in the dark; Louisa knew that. All the same there were shadows. They reached out after you. They closed in behind, so you did not dare turn your head. And the corridor was long, much longer than it ever seemed by daylight. It stretched and stretched. It seemed as if you would never get to the end.

The entry door was closed. Louisa tugged at it. It did not stir. She tugged again and it gave suddenly, with a creak that seemed to echo through the whole house.

She was in the chapel entry. There were no candles burning. Everything was dim and mysterious. Only a faint, uncertain flicker came from the little red swinging lamp overhead, shining down on the pine trees, the tiny house and the small waxen figure of the holy child.

For a moment, in that dim, pinkish glow, Louisa stood uncertain, her heart beating very fast. Then she moved closer, nearer still, till her fingers touched the white tablecloth. Resolutely she reached out her hand, snatched the holy child from his straw bed, and thrusting him into the warm folds of her dressing gown, turned and ran.

In the morning Louisa woke early. She pushed her hand under her pillow, where she had put the holy child to sleep the night before, wrapped up in a handkerchief to keep him warm.

Something very awful had happened to the holy child. No one would have recognized him. His limbs had lost their shape; his face was flattened and stuck fast to the handkerchief. He was nothing but a horrible messy lump of softened wax.

It was a judgment. She had been a wicked little girl. Hastily, too conscience-stricken even for tears, she folded the handkerchief back over what had been the holy child. But somehow through her misery a sense of injustice struggled. She hadn't wanted to be wicked; she had wanted to be good. She wanted to make the holy child warm and comfortable. She thought he would understand, and he hadn't understood. He had melted.

What could be done? She couldn't leave him there. She couldn't put him back into the chapel. Had there only been an earthquake, then and there, if it could have buried her and the whole school and the holy child all together so that nobody, nobody would ever know what had happened . . . But earthquakes didn't come like that. And the dressing bell was ringing . . .

The Ancient Mariner, with the dead albatross hung about his neck, suffered nothing in comparison with Louisa that morning. He at least did not have to carry his burden secretly. He was not in terror every moment that someone would say, "What's that lump inside your frock?"

Louisa seemed to hold herself rather queerly all morning. At recess she showed an inclination to sit alone and sniff. The young nun who was in charge of the children called her over.

"Why aren't you playing with the others, dear?"

"I—d'know. I think I got a cold."

"You shouldn't sniff like that. Where's your handkerchief?"

"I—haven't got one."

Louisa flushed guiltily. It was a lie. She knew where her hand-kerchief was. Even as she said it she could feel something slip-ping . . . slipping . . . right down by her waistband. If only the elastic would hold!

"Then I think you had better go and fetch one. Go quietly up and quietly back, and if you meet anyone on the stairs you can say that Sister sent you."

No sign from a relenting heaven could have been more welcome.

Clutching her waistband, treading with every precaution till she was once outside the door, Louisa went. Once she reached the corridor she flew, still gripping her garments tightly to her. All the morning she had prayed for just this chance. When she reached the dormitory landing she turned neither to left nor right but went straight on to the bathroom.

This particular bath had been put in when the school was re-modeled. It was a high, old-fashioned tub, and underneath it, where the pipes went down, there was a piece of floor board missing. Louisa knew this, for she had once lost a big glass bead down there. It had rolled under the bath and she couldn't get it out. What she was going to do was wicked, but it couldn't make things any worse than they were already.

She groped, shook herself; something fell with a little thud to the linoleum. She picked up the holy child, handkerchief and all, and lying down flat on her stomach she poked him through the hole and as far in under the floor boards as she could reach.

She had done with taking care of him. She had done with trying to be kind to people, ever again, as long as she lived.

Four o'clock came. Two by two the little girls went into chapel. As they passed the holy child's house, with the candles blazing before it, Louisa never turned her head. Invisible strings were pulling her, but she dared not look.

Nothing had been said all day. Perhaps in chapel they were go-ing to speak about it. Perhaps, when they all stood up to go out, someone would step out into the aisle . . .

But still nothing happened. The little girls rose, filed one by one out of the straight pews and joined their ranks, just as usual.

Louisa looked straight ahead. She crossed the mat by the chapel door. Now she could smell the evergreens and the hot wax; the warm breath from the candles was right in her face. She had to turn.

There was a little house, just as usual. There were Sister Gertrude's mountains, all shiny, and the pine trees and the shepherds and the gray donkey. And there, just where he always had been, was the holy child. He seemed to have grown a little, that was all. The candlelight shone on his yellow tight little curls and his waxen arms stretched out. He smiled at Louisa as if nothing had happened at all.

BY MARGERY WILLIAMS BIANCO

INDEX

Adeste Fideles, 124
Andersen, Hans Christian, 229-237
Animals of Christmas legends, 101-102, 105-106; *see also* camels, chickens, cows, deer, goats, lambs, reindeer
ANNIVERSARY, 204-213
Away in a Manger, 140, 141, 142

Bees, legend of, 105
Befana Fair, 112
Bells, legends of, 42-43
Bethlehem, Judea, 20
Bethlehem, Pa., 73, 76
"Bethlehem cave," 67
Bianco, Margery Williams, 243-250
Bird legends, 102-104; *see also* canaries, wrens
Boar's head, 94
BOY IN NAZARETH, THE, 198-203
Bozhitch, 110
Brooks, Phillips, 137-138, 139

Cakes, Christmas, 93, 96, 98, 99
Calendars, New and Old Style, 23, 111
Camels, 105
Canaries, 104
Candlemas Day, 78
Candles, Christmas, 77-80
Carols, history of, 119-121
Ceppo, 87
Chickens, 104
Christ Child *see* Jesus Christ
Christkindel, 114
Christkindli, 114
Christmas: dates, 23; first, 22; history, 23-28; in Elizabethan days, 26; prohibited by law, 27; *see also* animals, customs, decorations, fires, food, gifts
Christmas Hymn, A, 172
Christmas Love Feast, 78
Cookies, Christmas, 96, 97, 98, 100
Cows, 102

Crèche: first, 32-33, 68; in Europe and America, 68-74

Customs, Christmas: in Albania, 99; in America, 24-25, 28, 67, 72-74, 75-76, 78, 81, 84, 86, 90-92, 100-101, 103; in Argentina, 105; in Australia, 85; in Belgium, 96, 102, 104, 105, 109-110, 112; in Bethlehem, 28; in Bulgaria, 82, 98, 110; in China, 81; in Czechoslovakia, 98, 111; in Denmark, 80, 97, 103, 106, 110; in England, 79, 82, 84-85, 89, 94-95, 105, 106; in Finland, 79, 81, 85, 97, 111; in France, 69-70, 79, 82, 85, 96, 102, 109, 111, 114; in Germany, 70, 79, 82, 89, 96, 104, 105, 109, 110, 114; in Greece, 82, 99, 111; in Hawaii, 90; in Holland, 76, 96, 109-110, 114; in Hungary, 98; in India, 89; in Ireland, 79, 103-104; in Italy, 35, 68-69, 79, 82, 87, 97, 102, 112-113, 114-115; in Latvia, 99; in Lithuania, 89; in Mexico, 70-72, 77, 79, 85, 99-100, 110, 113, 114; in Norway, 79-80, 85, 89, 97, 101-102, 103, 105-106, 110; in the Philippines, 114; in Poland, 86-87, 89, 98; in Portugal, 97; in Rumania, 76, 93-94, 98; in old Russia, 98, 104, 106; in Scotland, 96, 102; in Serbia, 80, 82-83, 87, 98, 110; in Spain, 70, 79, 97, 102; in Sweden, 41, 76-77, 97, 103, 105, 110; in Switzerland, 98, 104, 110, 111, 114; in Syria, 78, 81, 105, 113; in Yugoslavia, 80, 102, 112

Daisy legend, 46-47
Day of the Three Kings, 105, 111
Decorations, Christmas, 84-92; *see also* holly, mistletoe, trees
Deer, 101
Discarded Christmas Tree, 176
Doughs, bread, 93-94
Druids, 49, 83-84

Epiphany, 77, 97, 105, 111-112; *see also* Twelfth Night

Farjeon, Eleanor, 162
Father Christmas, 58, 61, 111
Feast of Lights, 75
Field, Rachel, 176
FIR TREE, THE, 229-237
Fires, Christmas, 80-83
Fireworks, 81
Fish, 97, 98
Fisher, Aileen, 166
Flowers: as decoration, 85-86; legendary, 43-48
Food, Christmas, 92-101; *see also* boar's head, cakes, cookies, doughs, pies, plum pudding, smörgåsbord, wassail bowl
Frankincense, 19, 21-22
Frost, Frances, 164

Garden of Eden, 52
Gifts, 108-115
GIFTS FOR THE FIRST BIRTHDAY, 194-197
Glastonbury thorn tree, 53
Goats, 105-106
Gold, 19, 21
Good King Wenceslaus, 147, 148-149
Grandfather *Koleda*, 110
Gruber, Franz, 154-155, 156-157

Hardy, Thomas, 172
Hark! the Herald Angels Sing, 131, 132
He Came All So Still, 163
Herrick, Robert, 82
Hertha, 80
Hobby horse, 106
Holland, Josiah G., 119
Holly, 84, 85
Hopkins, John Henry Jr., 143-144, 145

I Heard the Bells on Christmas Day, 149, 153
Icicle legend, 52-53
It Came upon the Midnight Clear, 136

Jeslicky, 67
Jesus Christ: birth, 19-20, 23; giver of gifts, 113-115; in legends, 46-48,
    50-53, 98, 102-103, 105; and St. Christopher, 57
Joy of Giving, The, 163
Joy to the World, 128
Jule-nissen, 110

King, Emilie E., 198-203
Knecht Rupprecht, 110
Krippe, 70
Kris Kindle, 27

La Befana, 33-35, 112
Lambs, 102
Legends, 33-35, 42-53, 88, 101-106
Lights, Christmas, 75-83
LITTLE BLIND SHEPHERD, THE, 179-193
Little Christmas, 111
LITTLE GUEST, THE, 243-250

Littlest camel, 105, 113
Long, Elizabeth-Ellen, 176
Longfellow, Henry Wadsworth, 149-152, 153, 174
Lord of Misrule, 26
Lucia Bride, 41
Luther, Martin, 49-50, 88, 140-141

Magi *see* Wise Men
Mary, Mother of Jesus, 20; and greedy woman, 35-39
Mendelssohn, Felix, 131
Mistletoe, 49, 84-85
Mohr, Joseph, 154-157
Moore, Clement C., 63, 106
Morley, Christopher, 238-242
My Gift, 173
Myrrh, 19, 22

Nacimiento, 67, 70, 100
Nativity, 19-22
Neale, John Mason, 147, 148

O, Come All Ye Faithful, 121-124
O Little Town of Bethlehem, 138, 139
O Morning Star, 75
O Tannenbaum, 49, 92
Old Christmas, 111
Oxen, The, 172

Papa Noël, 111
Pastores, 77, 114
Peabody, Josephine Preston, 165
Peace of Christmas, 101-102
Pelsnichol, 110
Pickthall, Marjorie L. C., 214-221
Pies, Christmas, 94
Pinata, 113
Pine tree legend, 51
Plum pudding, 95
Poinsett, Dr. Joel Robert, 48, 86
Poinsettia: legend, 47-48, used as decoration, 86
Posada, 67, 70-72, 113
Post-Christmas Rhyme, 176
Presepe, 69, 79
Putz, 73-74

INDEX

Quetzalcoatl, 110

Reindeer, 106-107
Rose legends, 43-45
Rosemary legend, 45-46
Rossetti, Christina G., 172, 173

St. Basil, 111
St. Bonaventure, 121
St. Boniface, 49
St. Christopher, 57
St. Francis, 31-33, 68, 119, 121
St. Lucia, 39-41, 111; Day, 40-41, 111
St. Nicholas, 27, 58-64, 105, 108-110; Day, 58, 63, 98, 105, 110
St. Stephen's Day, 97, 103
Sangster, Margaret E., 204-213
Santa Claus, 27, 58, 63, 64, 106-107, 108, 111, 115
Santo Nino, 114
Saturnalia, 24, 83, 92
Sawyer, Ruth, 161, 194-197
Sears, Edmund H., 133-135, 136
Sharp, George, 179-193
Silent Night! Holy Night!, 157
Sing Hey!, 167
Sinter Klaas, 27
Six Green Singers, 162
Smörgåsbord, 97
Song of a Shepherd-Boy at Bethlehem, The, 165
Spider legend, 52
Stars, Christmas, 75-77
Suddenly Flowers in the Meadow, 166-167
Svaty Mikulas, 111

Three Kings *see* Wise Men
Three Kings, The, 174-175
To a Christmas Tree, 164
TREE THAT DIDN'T GET TRIMMED, THE, 238-242
Trees, Christmas: decoration, 88-92; famous, 91-92; legends, 49-53, 88
Twelfth Night, 85, 96, 111
Twelve Days of Christmas, The, 168-171

Ukko, 111
Urn of Fate, 113

Visit from St. Nicholas, A, 63-64, 107

Wade, John Francis, 122, 124
Wainamoinen, 111
Wassail bowl, 95, 120
Watts, Isaac, 125-127, 128
We Three Kings of Orient Are, 143, 145
Wenceslaus, King, 146-147
Wesley, Charles, 129-131, 132
Whittier, John Greenleaf, 163
Wise Men, 19, 21-22, 34-35, 45, 75, 105, 111-112, 143
Woodcutter legend, 50-51
Words From an Old Spanish Carol, 161
WORKER IN SANDALWOOD, THE, 214-221
Wrens, 103

Yates, Elizabeth, 222-228
YOUNG HANS CHRISTIAN ANDERSEN, THE, 222-228
Yule, 82, 92
Yule log, 81-83, 120
Yultomte, 110